D1154991

ALASKA

pioneer state

THOMAS NELSON & SONS

ALASKA

pioneer state

Norma Spring

photographs
Bob and Ira Spring

Alaska daily cruise ship "Sea Crest" visits Plateau Glacier, one of 20 big ones reaching sea level in Glacier Bay National Monument.

All photographs are by Bob and Ira Spring with the exception of the following from: Alaska Travel Division, p. 203; Humble Oil Company, p. 103; Seattle Times, p. 53; U. S. Fish and Wildlife Service, p. 111. Permission is gratefully acknowledged.

Second printing, March 1968

© 1966 by Norma Spring and Bob and Ira Spring

design by Harold Leach

Library of Congress Catalog Card Number: AC 66–10226

Printed in the United States of America

Foreword

With Alaska celebrating the centennial of its purchase from Russia, Norma Spring's "Alaska: Pioneer State" is timely and useful. It is a comprehensive description of what our 49th state is like today, who are the diverse people that constitute its citizenry, how it became what it is, and where it is likely to go in the future.

Mrs. Spring has produced a volume that covers nearly every aspect of contemporary life in Alaska, and is engagingly readable. It traces the history of Alaska from its discovery by Vitus Bering's expedition in 1741 into the seventh year of statehood. It contains a description of all the principal communities; of the highways and other means of transportation—air and maritime. It details the characteristics of the various ethnic groups that make up Alaska's one-fourth of a million people—Indians, Eskimos, Aleuts (the aboriginal inhabitants) as well as the more numerous later migrants from the "lower 48" and the "Old World."

Probably the high spots are the intimate depiction of several interesting groups of people who are doing things that are uniquely appropriate and characteristic of Alaska. They are the Carl Heinmillers, of Port Chilkoot, who, with their Chilkat dancers, are reviving the Indian dances, and who, with the Ted Greggs, of the same community near Haines, are recreating and promoting the native arts and crafts, and doing it most artistically and authentically. Another group are Celia Hunter and Virginia Wood, who, as partners, are pioneering in a delightful tourist experiment at Camp Denali, just outside of Mount McKinley National Park, in full view of that great monarch of the North American continent, and providing the kind of "roughing it" accommodations of which Alaska needs more. One could only wish that more such pleasing and sympathetic groups could be similarly saluted in this estimable and alluring guide to contemporary Alaska.

Mrs. Spring's book is precisely what the centennial visitor will need to appreciate the galaxy of interest that awaits him, and which Alaskans, also, will want to read and keep on their bookshelves.

ERNEST GRUENING
U. S. Senator from Alaska

Camp Denali guests explore Wonder Lake. Mount McKinley rises through the clouds

6

Acknowledgments

If we took a vote among the six members of our family on the question "Where would you most like to go this summer?" the unanimous answer would surely be "Alaska." And chances are good that we *will* go there. The only one of us who can really qualify as a native-born Alaskan is the youngest, adopted at the age of two months from her home in the very shadow of Mt. McKinley to become a part of our family. She is Alyeska, our Alaskan husky dog. The rest of us would hope to qualify as true Alaskans in spirit, at least, on the basis of our close association with the state.

Fifteen years ago, my photographer husband, Bob, came down with "Alaska fever." It was highly contagious, spread to Terry, our three-year-old son, and me, and that spring we found ourselves heading up the beautiful Inside Passage by steamship. We still feel that route, passing through some of Alaska's most impressive scenery (the same route the State Ferry follows), is the perfect introduction to Alaska.

The trip tally to date stands at ten or twelve for Bob's half of our photography firm, and a couple for Ira, his twin brother and partner. Collectively, we have travelled by land, sea, and air, in all seasons and to all parts of Alaska. The result: an immense Alaska picture file—a wonderful memory jogger during the process of writing this book.

Collectively, our family has passed most of the tests that qualify residents as sourdoughs: watched the midnight sun never quite sink into the horizon above the Arctic Circle on the longest day of the year; been awed by the mysterious play of the northern lights; flown to remote lakes for twelve-pound rainbow trout; seen grizzlies, moose, and caribou "right over there"; roamed the streets of historic gold-rush towns; panned gold with an old time Yukon prospector; chipped ice from our water bucket on the Klondike; fished for king crab out in the Aleutian Islands in a snowstorm; landed on a one-way bridge with a bush-flying State Senator; ridden in an Eskimo walrus skin oomiak on the Arctic Ocean; and sung and danced with the Chilkat Indian dancers.

Many of our Alaskan friends are mentioned in the book or appear in pictures; we are most grateful for their help, as well as their hospitality. Our special thanks to the following: the *Seattle Times* through articles by columnist Byron Fish and reporter Stanton Patty, for inspired Alaska coverage; our neighbor, Bob Henning, editor of *The Alaska Sportsman,* always good for some fascinating tales of Alaska, past and present; Ginny Wood and Celia Hunter, Alaskans, who waded through my very rough drafts; Alaskan authority, Dr. I. J. Montgomery, who so carefully read and commented on the finished manuscript; young Juneauite Mike Miller and the Alaska Travel Division never too busy to answer our queries or send us information he felt would be useful; our Edmonds library staff who saw that my every whim on research material was supplied.

And what would I have done without the remarks and reminiscences of all three children? Terry, Jackie, and Tracy's familiar "Did you remember to put in . . ." followed by something *they* thought was important about Alaska helped more than they realized.

Finally, my husband, Bob, without whom this book would never have been written—by me, at least. In choosing a life's work that the whole family can enjoy—travel photography—he has made it possible for all of us to go along and "help."

Though this book was aimed toward non-Alaskans with the purpose of informing them of the rugged past and present charm of this new state, we were very much aware of all the Alaskan friends looking over our shoulders. If those from the Outside like what they read and see we will be delighted. If Alaskans also like it, we will be *most* delighted.

Contents

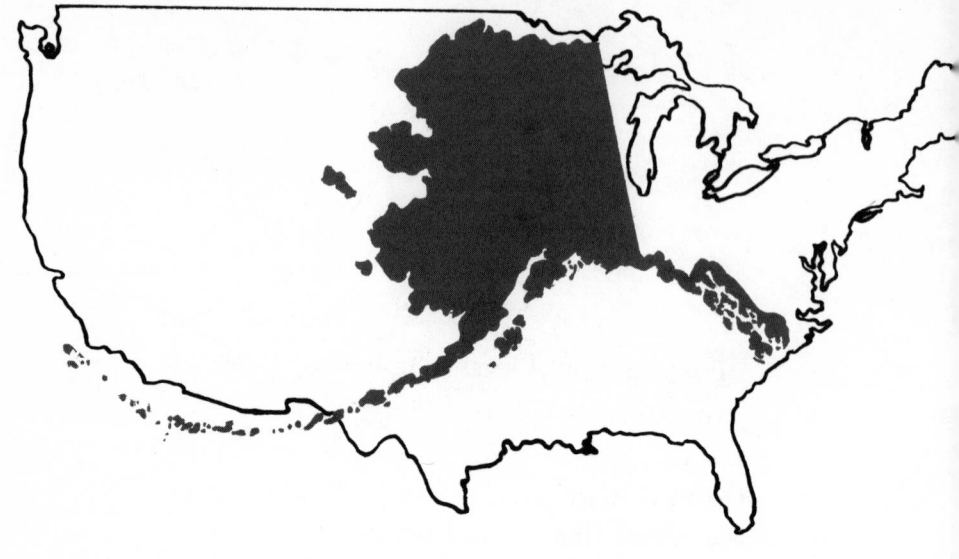

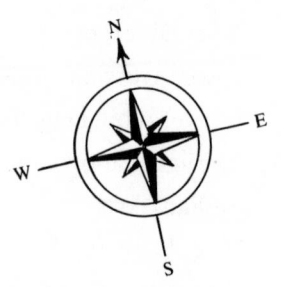

Alaska

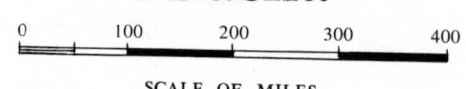

SCALE OF MILES

ATTU

ALEUTIAN ISLANDS

The Real Alaskans

Though twilight dusk denied the fact, it was midmorning, and the sprawling, snow-covered campus of the University of Alaska was fully awake. Here and there students, bulky in their warm winter garb, hurried to brightly lighted classrooms. The subzero temperature did not encourage lingering.

Nancy Plotts, her pretty, pert Eskimo features framed in the wolverine trim of her parka, dashed out of the women's new dorm and across the parking lot just as Phil Holland drove up. He carefully parked by a parking-meter-like object, got out, and plugged in a cord from his car radiator.

"Good to see you *cheechakos* getting in the habit of using those car-warmers," Nancy chided. "It's at least thirty below today."

"I learned the hard way last December," Phil answered good-naturedly. "And who are you calling a *cheechako*? After all, this is my second winter up here."

Together they headed toward the museum for their first class, their boot-clad feet making a soft squeaking sound in the dry snow.

"Here comes old leather-lungs," remarked Phil, as their ears picked up the distant, wild yelping of a dog team. "Think he has a chance to win the Fur Rendezvous dogsled races this year?"

Far off in the distance, a stocky young Eskimo hove into view, running behind and guiding a wooden sled with two waist-high handles, drawn by a team of six magnificent huskies. As they approached their

Nancy Plotts is hostess and narrator on stern wheeler "Discovery" in summer; goes to school at University of Alaska in winter

destination, the dogs' yipping became more joyous, and waves and greetings from fellow students followed them like the plume of soft snow tossed in their wake.

"If stamina and practice have anything to do with it, he should," answered Nancy. "I'll bet he has leg muscles like steel springs under those fancy mukluks his grandmother made him out of that walrus he got last spring."

"He made pretty good time this morning. No rabbits to lead his team astray, I guess," chuckled Phil.

"Are you dancing somewhere today or just trying to keep warm?" Nancy called to a tall Indian youth hurrying in their direction. His arms were full of masks and dance rattles, and over his shoulders was draped a fringed, shawl-like, mostly yellow blanket in bold Indian design.

"Both," smiled Frank Berry from Port Chilkoot and a member of the Chilkat Indian dance group there. "But I'm returning this blanket to the museum for safekeeping. Being responsible for a thousand dollar heirloom like this makes even *me* nervous!" And together they entered the building.

An Eskimo waitress wheels to work in Kotzebue. Motor scooters are becoming popular in native villages with limited roads

14

Campus of the University of Alaska near Fairbanks. Long summer days encourage floral displays and sightseers

The dog-sledder staked his team off-campus near some drifts, and the huskies promptly burrowed down for their accustomed snooze, while their master headed for class. As he drew near the museum, he was overtaken by an averaged-sized, sturdily built fellow rhythmically gliding over the snow on long, narrow, cross-country skis. His black straight hair and ruddy dark complexion indicated his native background.

"Are you getting in condition for the cross-country ski races?" the sledder greeted him.

"I can only hope; made fifteen miles this morning," replied the skier. "Say, I had to cut yesterday. What's the subject for today?"

"Right up your alley: natives of the Aleutian Islands."

"Let's go. I was wondering when that anthropology professor was going to get around to *my* family."

15

So starts a typical winter-semester day at the University of Alaska, just outside of Fairbanks, metropolis of the Alaskan Interior. For sure, it will be cold; temperatures have been known to drop as low as –60°. And though the day will become somewhat brighter, the hours of sunshine and daylight are short, three to four hours at most, this far north in the dead of winter. But Alaskans expect and are prepared for these facts of northern life.

The four young people on campus are typical of the student body. Of more than 1200 students, only about 100 are native Alaskans. Over half of these are Eskimos; about one third, Indians, the rest Aleuts. These figures give some indication of the relative proportions of these native divisions in all of Alaska, Eskimos predominating. Besides *cheechako* Phil, who represents one of many white students from Outside attending the University of Alaska, the rest of the college population consists of the sons and daughters of people who call Alaska home.

Like Will Rogers, a famous comedian of the 1930's, people with native blood are proud of the fact. Rogers, from Oklahoma, was never one to hide that he was a large part Cherokee Indian. Once when a dowager haughtily informed him that *her* ancestors came over on the Mayflower, he good-naturedly threw her the stopper which has become a classic: "Well, ma'am, *mine* were here to *greet yours!*"

Will Rogers has a counterpart in many Alaskans. About a sixth of the population there today can make the same boast about their ancestors. They were already there to greet the first explorers. Moreover, like our four students hurrying to anthropology class, they are interested in learning about their racial beginnings and culture.

Alaskan aborigines, the people living in Alaska before white men came, should be of interest also to Americans in the South-48 states, as Alaskans refer to states other than their own and Hawaii. There is a strong possibility the native groups forming a reception committee for new world explorers far to the south and two centuries earlier had the same ancestors as Alaskan natives.

Scientists believe there were no people on the American continent until fairly recent times, geologically speaking. Much evidence supports their theories that the first inhabitants migrated from Asia. Though an-

16

Eskimo in skin kayak used principally for hunting among broken ice floes in winter and spring

Indian fisherman near Port Chilkoot where there is a fish cannery

thropologists and historians do not agree exactly on timing, what are a few thousand years in the age of the world which is figured in millions of years? At any rate, those who study man and those who study his environment both agree that this is how it *could* have happened.

"The reason a family—or a whole village—started migrating in primitive days could often be traced to hunger," points out an anthropologist.

We can speculate that was what happened during the ice age, probably twelve thousand to twenty-five thousand years ago. As ice crept over the usual forage areas, animals were forced to seek new grazing grounds to the warmer south. Men naturally followed the animals—source of their food, clothing, and all else essential to their primitive existence.

How did both hunted and hunter manage to get across from the continent of Asia to North America? They probably walked across either on dry land or solid ice. The narrowest part of the Bering Strait, which separates the Asian and North American continents, is only fifty-four miles wide.

"During the long ice-age the water of the sea was held captive in large ice masses," theorizes one glaciologist. "There was only a two- or three-mile trickle to ford."

"By the time the glacier epoch reached its height thirty-five thousand years ago, the whole strait was frozen into a wide convenient highway," advances another.

Till recent times natives of the two Diomede Islands, only two and one-half miles apart (one Russian territory, the other American), took advantage of a similar route in winter, paying social visits back and forth. The lowering of the Russian iron curtain, however, put an end to this pleasant custom between these bewildered and isolated people. Closely related they may be, but their two countries are poles apart in politics.

Identical traces of prehistoric man as well as bones of prehistoric animals have been excavated on both sides of the strait—proof to support the migratory theory.

Now consider that these natives who started up in the very north-west corner of the American continent took thousands of years to migrate south and east. Primarily interested in survival, they were content to drift on to less rugged interior regions to settle wherever they could best work out their various destinies. Our own individual life span is such a speck on the world's timetable that it is hard for us to realize the effects that long periods of time and varying environments might have on people. They would eventually develop entirely individual cultures, language, and even physical appearance.

Thus, an agricultural people with a high degree of civilization were on hand to amaze the Spanish, first Europeans to explore this continent. And all American Indians are probably related because their forefathers originally came by way of the Alaska route.

The Spaniards, after claiming the initial discovery of the new world, explored the accessible sections. They were not interested in a vague, unknown land far to the cold north. For considerable time thereafter, no one knew or cared whether or not the land was inhabited.

In modern times it is not surprising that the Russians, accustomed to living in a harsh land themselves and being the nearest neighbors, were the first to become curious about the land to the east. An expedition in 1741 discovered the Aleutian Islands. Then, and in later explorations, the Russians found that Alaska was inhabited by primitive people.

By cataloguing traits and characteristics, customs and culture, habitat and environment, the student can divide the native people of modern Alaska into four main groups, actually subdivisions of the original racial stock. One division includes the Aleuts, who occupy the islands and western part of the Alaskan Peninsula. The second is made up of the Eskimos, who live along the Arctic and Bering Sea. Indians make up the other two divisions: the Tlingit-Haida Indians in the southeast coastal region and the Athapascan Indians living in the Interior.

The Aleuts

"Can these people be Russian?" mused Vitus Bering watching kayaks approach his ship off the Aleutian Islands in the eighteenth century.

It was a natural assumption; the natives were expert boatmen and were close enough to Russian islands and mainland so they might have made their way to the chain of islands stretching out into the Pacific.

Later studies by anthropologists, however, indicate that the natives of the Aleutian Islands were not Russian, but an Eskimo offshoot of the ice-age migrations. They drifted down and settled in the milder parts of these islands and were still living in stone-age style when discovered by the Russians in 1741. To survive, these people had to have four basic things: boats, houses, fire, and weapons. They handmade all four out of available materials and then embellished and improved them.

They needed boats for transportation and acquiring food, much of which was derived from the water. The boats were ingeniously and durably made of skin. Youth had its status symbol even then; the goal of every boy was to acquire his own skin-boat. As soon as he was able to provide all the materials on his own and pay the women for the necessary sewing, he became a man and completely responsible for his own welfare.

He needed protection from the weather, and his house was made of sod. In this house he needed a lamp for heat, light, and some cooking. The blubber lamp was the answer, for how many centuries we can only guess. Made of stone with refillable oil base and replaceable moss wick, those you can see in museums are probably still as good as the year they were manufactured.

His fourth basic necessity, weapons, was a step up from the simple dart and spear, called a "spear-thrower." It was a narrow flat stick with one end prepared to hold the shaft of the dart or spear. Use of this holder increased the power of the thrower's arm, and the men became very skillful hunters and fishermen.

These people industriously gathered food during the summer for feasts and celebrations in the winter. The women were noted for their beautiful sewing and basketry. They were not satisfied just to make garments and baskets practical; they had to be beautiful as well. Samples of clothing in museums are all the more amazing when you consider they were sewn entirely with needles made from the tiny bones of birds. Many of the items were perfectly watertight.

"The Aleuts were thirty thousand strong when the Russians came—it says here," quoted an Aleut student. "We've really been whittled down in the last couple of hundred years!"

20

Betty Wescott, guide at University of Alaska Museum, is Eskimo; she also has French and Norwegian blood. Map indicates location of native groups

Exploitation of the Aleut people by early Russian traders was greatly responsible for their fast diminishing number. Those that are left are mostly of mixed blood and live in the Pribilof and Aleutian Islands or in the larger Alaskan cities.

The Eskimos

Surrounded by a group of museum visitors, Betty Westcott—Eskimo and anthropology major at the University of Alaska—pointed to a large map.

"My people live in the Kuskokwim River area—here," she said. "They migrated from the Bering Sea during a time of famine, long ago."

Betty, who also can claim some French and Norwegian blood along with her predominantly Eskimo background, was a guide at the University's museum.

"Many people think of Eskimos as being only up on the Arctic Coast, in the land of the midnight sun," continued Betty. "Actually, they are a very mobile people, adept at both land and sea travel."

21

Even in ancient times, Eskimos were notably avid travelers. This explains why offshoots of the Arctic Eskimos are found away from the coast in the large river valleys to the south. In the course of a year, they moved from winter homes to summer camps, the better to accumulate and prepare the next winter's food supply. Sometimes the annual migrations added up to several hundred miles as they hunted game or visited other settlements.

This need for being sociable and communicating with other human beings was a strong incentive for travel. It meant a lot to isolated Eskimos to know that they had relatives at far distant villages. Paul Green, Eskimo writer, explained that the practice of trading or lending wives on visits was to give the children more brothers and sisters. Parents felt it was comforting to a child to know he might have many half-brothers or sisters in other parts of a barren world. And when he traveled, he was every bit as welcome in his foster family as in his own.

But the customs of the Eskimos in the old days were dictated mostly by the bleak, cold environment. A wife, or the loan of one, was essential

Old-time Eskimo reindeer herder and his wife. Eskimo wives were important partners on hunting expeditions

when a man was away from his own people, not only for companionship, but also for his creature comforts. Out of doors each person lived in his own small insulated world. Any break in his clothing, like a small hole in a mukluk, could spell disaster if there was no wife to mend it.

Today being able to survive, adapt, and accept changing conditions has been a real advantage to the Eskimo. Perhaps that is why there are more Eskimos now in Alaska than any other native group. Regardless of some individual differences, there are enough similarities in appearance, bone structure, customs, and language to class about one half of Alaska's native population as Eskimo. They are more readily absorbed into the white man's way of living and, through education and ability, are taking their place in the economic world.

The Indians

"It does look like Abraham Lincoln, all right, but how come he's on an Indian totem pole?" Jackie Spring queried Edward Keithahn, longtime curator of the Alaska State Museum in Juneau.

The young visitor was studying the weathered, unpainted, partly deteriorated carved figure. The brim of the tall hat was gone as well as the arms, and dried plant life fell from a pocket, adding to the seedy appearance of the frock coat. Even so, there was no mistaking the beard and profile of Honest Abe.

"The Indians who carved the tall monument to the President of the United States knew little about him as a politician or lawyer," explained the curator. "They wished to honor him when they somehow learned he was responsible for freeing them from slavery."

Likewise Lincoln probably had no idea that the amendment doing away with slavery in the United States would affect the status of Indian slaves in Alaska. Two years after the Civil War was fought, the United States bought Alaska from Russia. Consequently, the Thirteenth Amendment also freed many Indians living a life of slavery under more powerful Indian tribes in Southeast Alaska.

Over two hundred years ago white men other than Russians also explored the northwest Pacific coast. In Southeast Alaska they found various tribes of Indians living well off the bountiful supply of food provided by rivers and sea and mountain slopes. Their culture was highly developed and artistic. Houses were substantially built of wood, and though the people periodically visited traditional hunting and fishing grounds, their village was their permanent home base. The men were expert boat builders and seamen, a necessity in their way of life.

The Tlingits lived in the coastal region of Southeastern Alaska and were closely related to other neighboring coastal Canadian Indians in appearance as well as in culture and mechanics of living. Some other tribes had musical names like Haida, Tsimshian, and Tagish in Alaska; and their neighbors were Kwakiutl, Bella Coola, Salish, and Nootka tribes. They traded together and also fought over land, fishing grounds, and slaves to do the menial tasks.

"Women of the tribe were unusually well treated and highly thought of," fair-skinned Teresa Porter, a Tlingit who originally came from Yakutat, will inform a questioner proudly. "A man's place on the social scale and even wealth was passed down the woman's side of the family."

The Indian society at the time the white man came was an affluent one. Signs of wealth and plenty were apparent, and the people were interested not only in acquiring material things but also in displaying them. Amount of treasure had a lot to do with the social importance of an Indian. By giving a party—called a potlatch—and distributing gifts to all the guests, he declared his worthy name and acquired his social standing. Those with the most wealth were assured of a high status.

White traders and explorers observed the potlatch with amazement. The custom appeared to them to be quite devastating. If you had a rival and wanted to cut him down to size, you gave a big party, or potlatch, for him. Then it was his turn to give one back—only it had to be much bigger and better! No blood was spilled; the one with the most goods conspicuously wasted them on his rival and on the other villagers at the same time—to their delight—till his opponent was out of the running because of financial ruin.

This interpretation, though perhaps not quite the one the Indians had in mind, was amusing and still persists. Actually, potlatches are still held today but not on such a large scale. The emphasis has shifted, and now they are most often given to honor a recently deceased chief or to honor a new chief. The potlatch is still a big, elaborate party, but easier on the pocketbook.

The Athapascan Indians, living to themselves in one locality and inland, were the last to be influenced by the coming of white men. They were even left alone by the coastal tribes, who probably considered them too poor to make it worth the effort of invading them.

The "Come-Latelys"

The native people of Alaska today are just a fraction of the state's total population. Six out of every seven people are not part of the four original Alaskan subdivisions. They came from somewhere else in the United States, or from anywhere in the world.

"When people learn I am from Alaska," laughs pretty Annette Gregg, attending college Outside, "they are full of questions—mostly about how we keep from freezing to death in all that ice and snow."

Unless one has been to Alaska or had contact with someone who has lived there, the general picture is likely to be not only vague, but ridiculous. To the question "Who *does* live in Alaska?" the first answer is likely to be "Eskimos." And the person is thinking of parka-clad people living in a vast, snowy, icy wasteland. If he has been reading stories by Rex Beach or poems by Robert W. Service, he'll add "grizzled gold miners and prospectors."

During World War II, Alaska was in the news when the Japanese tried to use the Aleutian Islands for convenient stepping stones to a toehold in continental United States. Then, in nine months' time, the famous Alaska Highway was smashed through a thousand miles of utter wilderness as a defense measure. Thus the answer to "Who lives in Alaska?" might be "soldiers" or "construction workers."

These answers are not all wrong, by any means, but to the list must be added descendants of Russian, Norwegian, Spanish, British, and French explorers and gold-rush old-timers. And do not omit the homesteaders, government workers, home and business construction-laborers, businessmen, students, adventurers—transplants all, but nonetheless Alaskans.

Annette Gregg of Port Chilkoot competes for "Alaska State Ferry Princess" title. Member of Chilkat dancers, Annette attends college Outside but expects to return to Alaska

Finally, one last group, the young people: born there, growing up there, and planning their future in Alaska. Are these, perhaps, the only ones who can lay claim to being the *real* Alaskans?

The Spirit of Alaska

As the saying goes "Old soldiers never die" and neither does the spirit of old Alaskans. It keeps cropping up in their descendants and rubbing off on adopted residents. Out of the varied racial and national backgrounds of homesteaders, pioneers, adventurers and all others succumbing to the lure of Alaska emerges a composite picture of today's Alaskan. Basically the people share certain stubborn traits, or they would not be living in Alaska in the first place.

"Sure, it took our family many years to prove up on our homestead," remarks teen-age Abby Lancashire, "but Rome wasn't built in a day, either."

The Lancashire family left Ohio and started from scratch on the Kenai Peninsula about twenty years ago. Larry Lancashire, her father, was a bomber pilot, shot down over Romania in World War II. While in prison, he read about homesteading in Alaska and decided that was *the* place to rear his family—if he ever got out.

"Mother and Dad had to walk us to the one main road to catch the school bus. They carried guns and sometimes used them!" Abby reminisced. "The country was really wild then, and moose would attack anything in the rutting season."

Homesteaders on the Kenai Peninsula. Larry Lancashire and his wife raised their family in distant log cabin but have recently built a modern house

Now oil wells and houses are sprouting around the Lancashires and they have graduated from their primitive self-built log cabin to a house with modern plumbing.

Independent and individualistic in their thinking, most Alaskans are extremely sociable and cooperative in relationships with each other and visitors to their state. If a person needs help, it could be a matter of life and death, and the tendency is to extend the helping hand first and ask questions afterward. Many a person touring Alaska during spring thaws remembers some Alaskan hospitality while he was waiting for a jelly-like road to be made passable.

Take, for example, the experience of law professor Ralph Johnson of Seattle.

"I first met Rick Lauber, magistrate of Ketchikan, as we were driving off the State Ferry in a pouring rain." Mr. Johnson testifies. "Rick not only personally drove out to show us where to camp, but invited our whole family in to have breakfast and dry out the next morning!"

New treat for young homesteaders in the old Lancashire cabin. Water was heated on the stove and poured into tub

Alaskans are somewhat gamblers at heart and they are used to taking losses and disasters in stride. After the 1964 Good Friday earthquake, in spite of devastating damage in some parts of Anchorage and nerve-wracking aftershocks as the land settled down, surprisingly few gave up and left. The almost universal attitude is to move full steam ahead on planning and rebuilding.

Another facet in the composite Alaskan character is a certain pioneer spirit of adventure and the realization that Alaska is still a place where this can be satisfied. The people who have been settling Alaska, first as a territory and now as it has emerged into statehood, had their counterpart in almost every other state in the South-48. During the Westward Movement rugged pioneers sought more elbow room and better opportunities. Each new state in turn suffered growing pains as it found its place in the nation. The people endured lawless and ruthless eras as they conquered, exploited, and developed the land. Native people were displaced, exterminated, overrun, and absorbed. Wresting a living from the land was never easy and it took a certain type of people to do it.

The differences between the pioneers in the South-48 and those in Alaska are more a matter of degree. Whatever hardships the pioneers encountered in moving westward, Alaska pioneers can top them. Promise of riches in furs and gold lured some of the worst people in the world—as well as the best—to Alaska. Exploitation and violence during exploration and territorial days would be hard to match.

The timetable for Alaska's development has depended on many physical factors, among them climate, terrain, and most of all its isolated position. From now on, growth will be increasingly dependent on human factors. A state of many resources, its people are its greatest asset. Overall they have a strong pride and absolute faith in the future of Alaska, the one remaining pioneer state in a jet age.

The Aleuts Had a Word for It

A few years ago the editor of a big newspaper called five of his best reporters into his private office.

"Fellows," he said, "we owe it to our reading public to give them a good, up-to-date description of Alaska, now that it has been voted into our great United States." He paused and shuffled through a five-inch stack of tourist literature until he found what he wanted.

"Besides, I just can't swallow all this fantastic stuff coming from that fellow up in the—" he peered closer, " 'Travel Divison of the Department of Economic Development and Planning of the State of Alaska.' "

He paused again, and the reporters shifted a little uneasily, thinking of their waiting deadlines, and wondering if this was one of those times when they were expected to volunteer. He didn't keep them in suspense. Pushing back his green eyeshade and swinging around in his swivel chair, the editor indicated a large map on the wall.

"This is Alaska," he announced. "It's a big beat to cover; our best bet is to give all five of you a crack at it. But I can't spare you all at once, nor for very long at a time. We'll handle it this way."

The boss walked to the map, studied it a moment, and then drew five circles, none overlapping. He numbered the circles and then passed out a number to each man.

"Any reporter worth his salt ought to be able to get the feel of his section by spending a day and a night there; at least, that's all I'm allowing you on your expense account. File your report with me when you return."

Typical pioneer homestead in Matanuska Valley. Airplane in the back yard belongs to the owner, a flying dentist

Within a week, the first reporter had flown to his southeast portion of the state and was back in the editor's office with a gift for the boss: frozen shrimp and smoked salmon.

"Ya, sure! Alaska's yust like the ole country," stated the reporter enthusiastically. His name was Johanson, and he was still dressed in a slicker, sou'wester hat, and boots, which he swore was the native costume because of considerable rainfall. His description was full of the beauty of deep fjords, snow-capped peaks, and green trees; boats; fishing and logging.

The second man, assigned to Southwest Alaska, had a puzzled expression as he approached the editor's desk.

"I could have sworn my pilot was lost and we were over Hawaii . . . all those smoking volcanoes . . . but no trees. Gentle hills, waving grass— and *sheep* grazing!" He handed the editor his report and his gift: a huge carton containing a four-foot across (pincer to pincer) King Crab.

"Nothing personal," he added, sprinting to the door. "Product of the land; I mean sea, you know."

The third man couldn't get away till just after Christmas. His assignment was Point Barrow on the Arctic Coast, an Eskimo community that is on the farthest north tip of the continent. Before New Year's he was back, painfully making his pilgrimage to the editor's office. He was wearing his bedroom slippers, and his hands were encased in woolen mittens.

"Frostbite," he apologized, "and I'm sorry, but I won't be able to type my report till my fingers are better. But I'll be glad to answer any questions."

"Well, how do *you* like Alaska?" queried the editor.

The reporter thought a moment and then took the plunge.

"If you are giving me a choice, sir, I'll *eat* mine in the form of that Baked Alaska dessert, from now on."

Then, like the spring ice-breakup on the Tanana River, the poor man poured forth a torrent describing his cold, dark, miserable expedition, that left the editor with his mouth open. The gist was, in that reporter's opinion, the United States had made a big mistake a hundred years ago paying money to Russia for such an unusable piece of real estate. He complained that it hardly got light enough to see anything; not that there was much to see—only snow and ice. If he hadn't been keeping an eye on his watch, he never would have known when he had used up his twenty-four hours.

There was no gift. On the way back, someone had thoughtfully chipped off a chunk of glacier ice for him to put in the office cooler. Unfortunately, however, there was a long stopover in a warmer climate, and it melted down to the iceworms. These he dumped out, figuring that, like sea serpents and abominable snowmen, no one would believe there *was* such a thing, anyway.

There was nothing really unusual about the fourth reporter's trip to the Matanuska Valley and Anchorage area. It was during harvest time, and his report sounded like any other South-48 farming community having a fair. Of course, the editor questioned his statistics on the size of the vegetables displayed, but the reporter had the foresight to bring some huge carrots and a twenty-five-pound cabbage to prove his point.

Anchorage, the reporter felt—already big and bustling—would be the match of *any* metropolis if it continued its rate of growth and provided it didn't get shaken by too many earthquakes, like the Good Friday quake of 1964. His opinion was that Alaska wasn't *much* different from any of the other forty-nine states.

The last reporter flew up to Fairbanks in the Interior at the north end of the Alaska Highway in midsummer, when there was daylight round the clock. There was so much going on he completely lost track of time. He came home only after an exchange of telegrams that went like this:

"Are you all right stop why don't you come home stop"

"Still waiting for night stop am exhausted stop"

"Expenses exhausted just stop"

Needless to say, his editor was most interested in *his* report. He told about midnight baseball games, Eskimo Olympic Games, and visiting dredges in nearby gold fields. He mentioned his research project on the gold-rush era. This was carried on mostly at the nearby gold ghost-town of Cripple Creek. There he panned for gold in the One-Below-Discovery mine, and spent hours examining the famous old bar and other antiques in the Malemute Saloon.

The editor was inclined to believe his whole story after the reporter backed up his statement concerning the very warm weather with a picture of the bank on Main Street registering 92° (above zero) on its thermometer sign.

"Funny," the editor mused, "I always thought that was a real cool place up there."

The reporter's gift of a small gold nugget to be made into a tie clasp, though well-received could not quite get him off the hook.

"Even if it *did* stay light," chided the editor, "I should think you *might* have noticed when people went to bed and judged a little closer when your time was up."

"Alaskans *never* sleep!" countered the reporter, and fell in a heap from sheer exhaustion.

By this time, you probably feel there is something familiar about the above story. It is a modern version of that very ancient story of the blind men trying to describe an elephant. By feeling and describing only one part, each came up with a different impression. However, pooling their information and perhaps encouraged to feel other parts, each man might finally arrive at a fairly accurate picture of the elephant.

That is just what our editor did with his elephant—Alaska. It was a successful series, judging from the number of letters he received. Some (mostly from long-time Alaskans) felt the reporters were not there long enough to be qualified to write about someone else's favorite state. This group also pointed out that too much should not be made of first impressions of a place; and that the man who went to the Arctic might have at least waited till it got light to judge the place, even if it took a couple of months.

Others from all over the country (these columns were syndicated) were pleased to learn more about the new state and to hear that everyone was getting along well after the big earthquake. Happiest of all was the Publicity Director of the Travel Division of the Department of Economic Development and Planning of the State of Alaska. He offered the editor the key to the capital, Juneau, and said their office had received so many inquiries on Alaska travel that they were expecting a record tourist season. The editor placed the accompanying inch-high stack of new Alaska literature in his circular file.

King crabs weigh up to ten pounds and measure five feet across. These are being cleaned for processing

King crab fishing boat maneuvers alongside processing ship at Adak in the Aleutian Islands

What's in a Name?

Primitive people are noted for using very few words to communicate ideas and describe people or places. Alaska says a lot in a small package, and we can thank some of the original Alaskans for coming up with just the right descriptive name.

The Aleuts, living on the string of islands stretching out into the Pacific almost to Russia, were well aware for ages of the large mass of land to the north and east of them. They summed it up in one word: *Alaxsxaq,* which meant the Great Land. Over the centuries the word was changed as it was passed down. In pronunciation, that is; there was no written language. The words sounded like Alyeska, Aliaksha, Aliaska, to mention a few variations. Today we have the simplified version Alaska. But no matter how it is spelled, the meaning is still apt. Though the Aleuts were referring to the size of this big land to the north, they also could have been thinking of the richness of the land. Richness to them, of course, meant the abundance of game and fish, necessary to their existence.

The Russians called this land during their sovereign rule Russian America. When they sold out to the United States, Congress officially named the newly purchased territory Alaska.

Today, translating Alaska as "the great land" conjures up visions of opportunities and potential wealth undreamed of by the simple natives. Past bonanzas in history, where explorers and adventurers made fortunes in furs and gold, spur today's speculators to search for other barely tapped resources.

Agriculture is still in an experimental stage and successful in some areas. Manufacturing possibilities, for home use as well as for export, have been explored successfully by only a few people so far. Sportsmen consider Alaska great for fishing and big game hunting. Already many people consider Alaska a fascinating place to visit every year and in all seasons. This has forced the expansion of the tourist industry and allied recreational facilities.

And as the growing population of this state indicates, a large number of people are deciding that Alaska is a great place to *live* and rear families.

Cow moose swims in small pool near Camp Denali. Mount McKinley, highest peak in North America, towers in the background

How Big is Big?

"If you Texans don't quit bragging about the size of your state down there, we'll cut Alaska in half and make Texas the *third* largest state!"

Quips like that are no idle boast; the forty-ninth state is more than twice as big as its nearest rival. In fact, Alaska is larger than the next three largest states put together: Texas, California, and Montana. Alaska contains 586,400 square miles, but this is nothing but a dull statistic to most people. It is hard to comprehend the size of an object unless you can compare its size with something familiar.

Petersburg, a fishing port on the Inside Passage, south of Juneau. Many Alaskans of Scandinavian descent live here

Take a map of the whole United States, for example. Each state is marked off, and you get some idea of the relative size of the various states. But up in the northwest corner is a sizeable state, too far from the others to compare easily. Cut this state right out of the map. Then place Alaska on the map of the whole United States, finding a spot where all of it, even the island strings, fits within the boundaries. It is plain to see that Alaska can cover one fifth of the whole United States.

What Time is It?

Measuring an object in space is not too hard, because the factors involved are usually things you can actually see. There is another way of measuring Alaska, using the dimension of time.

Science fiction stories about time machines which make it possible to travel back and forth in time, don't seem so far out anymore. Airplanes might be thought of as a kind of time machine. Air travel is now so speedy all over the world that a person at times experiences an eerie feeling of having been projected out of his time slot.

From east to west, Alaska has four different time zones in about twenty-seven hundred miles. Flying from Juneau, the state capital in Southeast Alaska to Nome, Arctic town on the Bering Sea Coast, a traveler has to set his watch back three hours, just as he would if flying from New York to San Francisco.

Traveling through the Aleutian Island chain, it is *almost* possible to skip twenty-four hours and move from today into tomorrow. Alaska extends even farther west than Hawaii. It stretches well into the eastern hemisphere, almost to the International Date Line. In fact, this date line was purposely made to jog westward so that all Alaskans could live the same day as the rest of the United States.

There are other superlatives that fit the state of Alaska besides biggest, farthest north, and most westerly. Alaskans are quick to point them out. Claiming the largest state horizontally isn't enough; Alaskans also claim the vertical title. One of their mountains, McKinley, with 20,320 feet elevation, is the highest on the North American continent. Ten more soaring Alaska peaks top the nearest rival, California's Mount Whitney. The thirty-four thousand-mile Alaskan coastline is longer than the rest of the continental United States's Atlantic, Gulf, and Pacific coast lines put together. And within its boundaries is found a most amazing variety of physical features.

An Overall Look at Alaska

Certain words have come to be associated with Alaska: ice, snow, Eskimos, Indians, furs, seal, salmon, bears, mountains, moose, tundra, walrus, ivory, cold, rain, dogs, gold, planes, oil, boats, whales, glaciers, grass, volcanoes, trees. By sorting out all these items, and many more, and placing them in their proper geographic positions, you would see that Alaska is made up of five distinct and varied sections.

One part is the Panhandle, as the narrow strip of Southeast Alaska is called. Another is the South Central division, where the greatest population is around Anchorage. This section includes the Kenai Peninsula and extends to Kodiak Island. A third section continues along the Gulf of Alaska Coast and on out the Alaska Peninsula clear to the most westerly tip of the Aleutian Islands. This tag-end section separates the North Pacific Ocean from the Bering Sea.

These three sections are set off by several mountain ranges that make up a long Coastal Mountain Barrier. They effectively block off a band of land in Alaska that is only a hundred miles wide at most, though it makes an arc over three thousand miles long.

The State Ferry leaving Peril Strait approaches landing near Sitka. This spectacular camp spot is on Harbor Mountain

Behind this mountain barrier, to the east and above the middle part of the arc, lie the last two divisions: the Bering and Arctic Coast and the vast Interior. These divisions are also set apart by mountain ranges.

If a traveler had the inclination, the time, and all means of transportation at his disposal it would be most fascinating to sample all these distinctive parts of Alaska. In some cases he might even wish for a magic carpet or a space ship! A logical sequence of travel would be to circle the state of Alaska completely, tracing the Pacific Ocean coast from the temperate southern part to the Arctic and then taking a look at the part within that circle. Then he would be ready for his space ship. A view from high above might be most enlightening in placing Alaska in its position with her sister states and with her world neighbors.

The Panhandle

If Alaska brings to mind the words ice, snow and sub-zero temperatures, you might as well forget them when you visit Southeast Alaska. Some ice and snow are much in evidence in this area, but mostly as part of the scenery. The mountains, never very far away in this part of Alaska, sport all sizes of glaciers and icefields. In ages past, the glaciers were responsible for carving the deep fjord-like coastline. The climate is mild, but wet. The heavy rainfall keeps the vegetation lush and green and the slopes heavily forested.

About three hundred miles north and west of Ketchikan, the coastline leads into the Gulf of Alaska Coast, and a changing scene in the Coastal Mountain Barrier.

Gulf of Alaska

For two hundred miles the coast is open to the ocean. The islands are gone, and only a narrow plain separates ocean and mountains. The mountains rise higher, the glaciers and snowfields become bigger, till all together they add up to the most extensive mountain mass in North America, the Saint Elias and Chugach Range. These are a real challenge to mountain climbers.

Then as the coast swings to the west, the appearance and nature of the Southeast zone comes back—but more so: green-wooded islands, glaciers and fjords. A rain trap, created by moist ocean winds being forced upward by the high mountains, dumps a fantastic amount of rain in some areas.

A small seaworthy boat might be a good choice for following the beach along the mountain barrier on this leg of the journey, past the relatively small towns of Cordova, Valdez and Seward, all important to Alaska's transportation industry at one time or another. Rounding the Kenai Peninsula, the traveler notes a change in character of the land as it takes on a somewhat pastoral look. Homesteaders are here on the Kenai, and also in the Susitna and Matanuska valleys, where many kinds of crops flourish in the long days of summer sun.

At the head of Cook Inlet lies Anchorage, largest city in Alaska. North through this valley system lies the main route through the mountain barrier to the Interior. The towns of this part of Alaska—Anchorage, Kodiak, Seward, Valdez and many smaller ones—were hardest hit by the Good Friday earthquake.

The Aleutians

No wonder the second reporter was bewildered after his jaunt through the Aleutian chain of islands. Alaska seems to go off on a tangent in character as well as in direction. The Aleutian Islands, south and west of the main body of the state, appear to be a range of partially submerged mountain tops. Peaks and glaciers are not so high as those passed earlier but are forbidding in their own way. Some are eroded mountain tops and some are topless because they were blown to bits by volcanic action. Others are active volcanoes, their cones frequently live and smoking! From the air it is easy to imagine that perhaps these *were* part of a bridge from the Asiatic mainland thousands of years ago.

Separate teams of scientists, one American and one Soviet, studying on opposite sides of the Bering and Chukchi Seas, very recently outlined their conclusions for a joint article in a science magazine. The two teams never met, but developed the article through correspondence. They be-

Jet-sized International Airport with Anchorage in the distance on Cook Inlet. International is one of the world's busiest airports

lieve sea levels were lower because the water was trapped and stored as ice in continental glaciers. Most of Northeast Siberia and Alaska were probably free of the ice and joined by a bridge of grassy plains eleven thousand to twelve thousand years ago, practically yesterday in geological time. These scientists agree that possibly the shallow parts of the Chukchi and Bering Seas have been dry land for much of the past one hundred million years. Thus, to the north, it is possible men roamed and

43

hunted freely on this grassy bridge, and those that kept on going were the first natives of North America.

The Aleutian Island zone appears grim. It is mostly grass country—green in summer, white in winter and in between, brown and desolate—with few, if any, trees. Violent, roof-shaking winds rip over the small, often fog-isolated villages dependent mostly on fishing and trapping. And though there are attempts to raise sheep and cattle on the one lush commodity, grass, it is a long way to market.

Attu Island, the southwest tip of this Alaskan chain, is the most western point in America. Ketchikan at the southeast tip of Alaska is over two thousand miles away and almost due east.

The Bering Sea Coast

The Aleutian chain seems quite detached from the rest of Alaska and more like a side trip. To pass through the mountain barrier and head up the Bering Sea Coast, we will return as far as Unalaska. Here the traveler runs into southern Arctic ice-floe territory. The sea lanes may be frozen or hazardous because of drifting ice much of the year. It may be necessary to hire a plane and bush pilot at this point. The alternative may be a guide, dogteam, and sled.

Two hundred miles to the north are the famous, and isolated, seal islands of the Pribilofs. Indenting the coast to the east of these is Bristol Bay, center of the sockeye salmon industry. From Bristol Bay the coast which has been heading west now goes north to Eskimo country.

Eskimos have lived in practically the same way for centuries in the domain of the big Kuskokwim River. The country is mostly flat with slow-moving rivers and thousands of lakes and ponds. These sub-Arctic River systems, including the Yukon, are the nesting grounds for most of the waterfowl in North America.

The coast continues to stay flat, but low mountains can be seen off in the distance. Past the mouth of the mighty Yukon River, beyond the Eskimo village of Unalakleet, and then the traveler approaches the north limit of the Bering Sea. Here is Nome, once a sprawling boom town, the scene of frantic gold-rush activity at the turn of the century.

The Arctic Coast

Wales, on the Bering Strait, marks the separation of the Bering Sea and the Arctic Ocean; on the outside edge of Alaska is the Arctic Coast. Following around the coast we find a few small Eskimo villages, and a major one at Kotzebue, twenty-five miles north of the Arctic Circle. Although the terrain is still mostly flat, there are sizeable mountains visible on the horizon, especially around the mouth of the Noatak River and Point Hope. Along the banks of the Noatak grow the last of the trees, some stunted spruce.

Then comes the true Arctic, a great coastal plain, snow-covered most of the year. Except in the short summer, it is hardly possible to tell where the ice of the Arctic Ocean leaves off and the tundra begins.

Tundra is a Russian word which means "where the trees are not." In the Aleutians and the Arctic, tundra means a hardy growth which survives where nothing else will. In the Arctic, it is the vegetation covering vast areas of permafrost.

Permafrost is ground which remains always frozen below a certain depth. It exists where the mean annual temperature is below 32° F. If the mean is even one degree above that, permafrost will not form.

An English visitor to the tundra-permafrost regions of Alaska coined her own apt definition: "Tundra is a botanical toupee for permafrost!"

The barren coast of Alaska continues along the Arctic Ocean and across the top of Canada.

The Great Interior

So far in this overall look at Alaska we have stayed only on the fringes. This fringe takes in only about two fifths of the total area. The rest, the Interior, lies between mountain ranges and among river valleys. Highways and railroads connect main towns of the central Interior.

These highways continue on through Canada to the rest of the United States. Even though the roads are long and pass through vast wilderness country, they eventually lead to the Outside. This comforting fact makes interior people feel less isolated than coastal people.

The Interior is far from being a flat plain. The many rivers are separated by mountain ranges of varying heights. Some of the valleys produce vegetables fantastic in size during the long summer daylight hours —almost twenty-four hours a day of sunshine.

The Interior is far from any large bodies of water that might moderate the climate. The temperature in Fairbanks, for example, has varied 111 degrees when measured on specific days a year apart! (A record low of $-59°$ on that day and a year later a record high of $+52°$.) Yet the climate is dry enough to require irrigation, and miners have complained about not having enough water for their sluice boxes and dredges, used to wash gold from sand and gravel.

Anchorage, the gateway to the Interior, is a seaport, but the climate there and the vegetation are more like the rest of the Interior than like the coastal regions.

How to Unscramble the Interior

"All those Alaskan names for the rivers, valleys, and mountains of the Interior can be pretty confusing. Here's *my* method for figuring out the geography," one visitor to Anchorage volunteered.

He suggested taking a map to the top of any skyscraper in Anchorage and using it as an orientation point.

"Consider yourself at the hub and face toward Fairbanks, which is four hundred miles to the north," he continued. "Of course you can't possibly see the whole Interior, even on a clear day! But as you study your map you can see how the major river valleys which shape the Interior fall into place like pieces in a giant jigsaw puzzle."

Obviously relishing the sound of the Alaskan names, the man warmed up to his subject. He pointed out the two largest, the Yukon River and the Kuskokwim, on the map and then indicated their approximate location behind Mount McKinley and the Alaska Range visible off in the distance.

"The Yukon is twenty-five hundred miles long and is made up of many rivers as it curves west across the Arctic Circle to reach the Bering Sea," he continued. "Fairbanks, second largest city in Alaska, is in the heart

The Yukon River meanders west of Fairbanks. A small Indian fishing village is located on the right bank

of the Interior in the upper Tanana Valley, one of the largest rivers feeding the Yukon system."

He mentioned the considerable boat traffic on the Kuskokwim, and as it flows south, the contrasts of rolling hills, trees, and portageable back rivers and sloughs in the valley. The closer river valleys were pointed out: Susitna, Matanuska and Copper along with their mountain range dividers: the Talkeetnas and Chugach.

He finished triumphantly with, "Even if you can't figure out where all this is and don't remember all the names, you'll have to admit this is a first-rate view from up here."

And it is; from beautiful, green farming country to Mount McKinley, towering among peaks of the Alaska Range, visible to the north on fine clear days.

47

Two Final Angles for Viewing Alaska

In our overall geographical look at Alaska we have traveled all around its perimeter. Then we took a bird's-eye look at the Interior. To make the inspection complete there are two more directions we can take: straight down and straight up. Both have been done to some degree.

The surface has already been scratched and a fortune in Alaska's most famous mineral, gold, has been taken out in a little over half a century. Now enterprising companies are digging a lot deeper. They are finding other buried treasure, including the new black gold (oil) and natural gas, even under the seas and ice floes.

The main reason for borrowing a space ship and traveling straight up is to look down on Alaska and surroundings to gain a perspective on how this over-sized state fits into the world neighborhood. From a rocket ship the foreign neighbors look very close.

Russia is two hundred miles to the west of the farthest tip of the Aleutian Islands. Siberia is just a plane hop over the horizon from Nome on the Bering Sea coast. But where the International Boundary runs between two small islands, the Diomedes in the Bering Sea, Russia and the United States are separated by less than three miles!

Japan's attempted invasion of the United States by way of the Aleutian Islands during World War II showed the importance of Alaska for our defense. Famous flying General Billy Mitchell stated: "I believe in the future he who holds Alaska will hold the world."

Bombers based at bustling airfields and outposts are within easy flying distance to any spot in the north half of the world today.

It is easy to see why Alaska's airports are International. The popular Polar Route is becoming as well known as the polar bear. It is indeed a shortcut to the capitals of Europe and Asia, with Alaska the logical stepping stone.

Actually, from Anchorage the route goes to the northeast of the Pole, skirting the upper tip of Greenland, over Scotland, and then southward to London.

"Alaska's future potential as a transportation center is even more promising," states Bill Marsh, an official of Pan American Airways. "Try · this experiment with your world globe."

He suggests putting one end of a string on New York, stretching it across to Tokyo, and then noting where the halfway mark falls. Fairbanks, at almost exactly the halfway point, would be the natural refueling stop in a route connecting two of the world's largest population concentrations: Tokyo and New York.

In these first two chapters we have talked about the two main ingredients of this pioneer state: the land and the people. The land, it appears, is still in the process of being shaped by nature, sometimes in violent and unexpected ways. The people are molded by the land, no matter how long they have been there nor where they came from originally.

Is Alaska a state fabulously rich in natural resources still to be discovered and used, as some people believe? Or does her future wealth lie in the field of transportation and services?

Some people feel Alaska is important for other, more intangible values. This view is held by those attracted to Alaska by her promise of space and wilderness and a chance to pioneer. They would like to keep it that way.

The discovery of Alaska's vast potential, wherever it lies, is up to her people—not as explorers, exploiters, or bonanza seekers, but as thoughtful and dedicated citizens.

The Violent Land

On March 29, 1964, Alaska experienced an earthquake analyzed in the year following as the worst on record in horizontal and vertical extent. The first mighty shock and over twelve thousand aftershocks in the following months released damaging energy comparable to the Hiroshima atom bomb. A general uplift of the sea floor, underwater rock slides, and buckling slopes caused giant destructive waves to batter the shoreline. These local waves preceded the far-reaching tidal waves that hit Seward, Kodiak, and other coastal communities as far away as Crescent City, California.

"Our later surveys showed some land was uplifted over thirty-one feet," said Captain Harold Seaborg of the Coast and Geodetic Survey. "Other land levels dropped almost six feet."

The first shock knocked out communications. Thus, a combination of too little information followed by far too much of the rumor variety in those first few days gave an extremely distorted picture of what was actually happening. Reports were grim, and the impression given was that the whole state was a total loss.

The first inkling of the earthquake came from a ham radio operator near Seattle, Washington, who happened to be talking to another ham in Anchorage. It was Good Friday. The stores had just closed, and people were homeward bound for the Easter weekend. The man in Anchorage mentioned that it appeared they were having a small earthquake. Then as it worsened, he shouted that the "ground was waving like an ocean."

Knife River cuts through two hundred feet of sand flow in the Valley of Ten Thousand Smokes

Communications broke off, and the Seattle man phoned the news to a radio station. He and many other amateurs then stayed at their short-wave sets, taking and relaying messages to anxious relatives and friends. There was no doubt that a catastrophe had occurred, but it was impossible to determine the extent till some time afterward.

Reporters and photographers were rushed to Anchorage and the other affected towns. They found much devastation to photograph and many appalling tales of personal experience and eyewitness reports to rush to the news-hungry Outside. It was verified that the disaster had indeed struck a crippling blow to a most vulnerable area. Anchorage, the center of a large percent of business and financial wealth in the state, is also Alaska's largest city. Fast growing in recent years, almost one half of the state's residents live in the area. Even discounting reports due to panic and rumor, there was still plenty of reason to suspect the worst.

By the time newsmen were out covering the disaster, most Alaskans in spite of the frightening aftershocks were already busily and determinedly picking up the pieces. One story making the rounds concerned a man from a national magazine sent to take pictures and report on the Turnagain Arm residential area. This beautiful, scenic Anchorage suburb of

Bustling Fourth Avenue, main street of Anchorage, before the Good Friday earthquake

The main street of Anchorage after the earthquake which destroyed two blocks of stores and a residential area

expensive homes was hard hit by the quake. The photographer spotted a couple salvaging belongings from the shambles of their home, the wife receiving household goods from her husband several feet down and invisible from the surface. The reporter interviewed the wife and stated the pictures he wanted. She called down to her husband that a man from *National Geographic* was there.

"Tell him we don't want a subscription," came the speedy and businesslike reply.

From the safe position of hindsight (and considerable time later) it is now possible to evaluate and assess the damage caused by the Good Friday earthquake of 1964 and place it in a proper perspective.

53

Perhaps the only predictable thing about earthquakes so far is the fact that they have always occurred, and they probably always will. It is the nature of our planet. No spot on earth is immune. Sometimes earthquakes occur deep under the seas and in isolated, uninhabited places and we never hear of them. The Bible mentions earthquakes, and they are part of the legends and folklore of primitive people. Some areas, in our particular geological time, are more prone to upheavals than others. Alaska, along with the whole Pacific Coast and other Pacific Rim countries, is considered to be in an earthquake zone.

In such an area when the earth starts quivering and shaking, the terror is indescribable. For a few seconds or longer, there seems to be no place to go or anything to do but wait and wonder. This time, is it but a small, earth-settling jolt? Or will the intensity and motion increase until lives are snuffed out and damage runs into the millions of dollars?

Facing up to such possibilities emphasizes again, what has been described as the basic nature and character of Alaskans. The people who choose to live there are quite aware of the hazards as well as of the advantages. They weigh these from their individual and personal viewpoints and are prepared, like boxers, to roll with the punches and come back fighting. People who settle in Alaska have long since made up their minds that their reasons for doing so outweigh any disadvantages that may arise. They are not about to be shaken out of their chosen state even by a major earthquake.

The first shocking headlines fearing six hundred dead and Anchorage leveled—and other coast cities possibly swept away by tidal waves—gave way to more realistic figures. The later tally of about one hundred and fifteen lives lost was miraculously low, though property damage came to millions of dollars. Though important, the part of Alaska affected—the Gulf of Alaska—is a very small area compared to the rest of the big state.

During the time of trial, almost every type of earthquake-triggered disaster occurred somewhere in the stricken area. Homes and highways and public buildings were destroyed, and utilities knocked out. Fires broke out, and there was no water with which to fight them. Some places had too much water from tidal waves and the recurring abnormally high tides. Some fantastic accounts of what happened later turned out to be true.

Eyewitnesses at both Valdez and Seward, port towns and important transportation and shipping centers, swore the bottom appeared to drop out of their harbors, swallowing docks and people. After measurements, the coast and Geodetic surveyors say that is exactly what happened. The only answer for Valdez is to relocate the town about one-and-a-half miles up the beach on higher ground and firm bedrock. Ironically, this was the original site planned for the town in 1897, but eager gold-rushers set up housekeeping as close as possible to the end of their trail and to their source of supply, the docks. As townspeople rebuild today, they are optimistic and look forward to gaining their town back—only better.

Tidal waves caused by the earthquake did tremendous damage to Kodiak and neighboring native villages where over seventy persons were killed or missing.

Kodiak, one of the oldest settlements, goes back to the days when Alaska was owned by Russia, and Kodiak was the political center (before Sitka) and headquarters of the rich fur trade. The waves freakishly uncovered a souvenir of these early Russian days when they swept away the Standard Oil Company pier. Now exposed is a stone seawall, built by the traders about 1792. It is remarkably solid. No cement then, the rocks were interlocked to hold them together. There are even a couple of ships' anchors imbedded in the wall. The rings on the shafts probably were used to moor the sailing ships. The local historical society intends to preserve the wall, as well as a three-story house on a hill nearby. In the late 1700's the house was the headquarters of Alexander Baranof, the governor of Russian America.

Besides loss of life, the tidal waves caused the loss of the small boat harbor filled with fishing boats. Fishing and big game hunting are the backbone of the town's economy. The fishing fleet was lifted by the powerful water as if the boats were toys. Eventually the ships were deposited high and dry in the center of town, but many were hopeless ruins. All required extensive repairs. Losing the most cherished tool of his trade is a low blow to a fisherman.

Alaskans are proud of gardens, enhanced by long mild summer days. This is part of Anchorage's "Turnagain by the Sea" district that was undamaged by the 1964 earthquake

Kodiak has already an impressive list of accomplishments. Town planners admit their town was on the dilapidated side, old and run down even before the earthquake. The chores of rebuilding are being attacked with the attitude that out of disaster also comes opportunity. With the help of Federal disaster funds and private capital, they are rebuilding a modern town. In addition to their usual industries, the townsmen feel they have much to offer tourists interested in history as well as recreation. They are no longer off the beaten track. The State Ferry System's Marine Highway now includes Kodiak as a port of call.

Anchorage

The big, sprawling city of Anchorage is an infant among cities in Alaska. It was a mere boat anchorage in 1914. Then the Alaska Railroad construction headquarters and survey camp founded the town and started it on its way to become a gateway for shipping to the interior. Growth was held back because of the problems of isolation. Costs of living were high, so that even by 1940 the population was still less than five thousand. World War II was the vitamin shot that started the infant city's phenomenally fast growth. Anchorage became the hub of defense, and Uncle Sam was its best customer.

Besides being a fast growing infant, it is also a tough baby. That is evident in the way the city has bounced back after the earthquake. A lot of damage was done, but the scars are hardly noticeable to the casual visitor. The residents pitched in with pep and enthusiasm on the job of rebuilding. Faith and determination were bolstered by the quick release of disaster funds for use on public facilities. The Small Business Administration came through with a liberal program for loans to enable private businesses to get back on their feet.

Today it is an international air center, and the city population has grown to about fifty thousand people—twice that, if the Greater Anchorage area is included. More than any other Alaskan city, the appearance and character of Anchorage are like those of other cities of the same size in the rest of the United States.

There are many signs evident of a booming economy. Shipping is on the increase; there are new oil and gas discoveries nearby, an iron-ore strike, the beginning of State Ferry service, and a strong tourist industry.

The skyline is constantly changing with more tall buildings going up. The J. C. Penney Company store that was wrecked in the quake has been replaced with one twice as big. The Westward Hotel, the Captain Cook Hotel, the Hill Building, the First National Bank, and other skyscrapers give a big-city look. Rebuilding is done with earthquakes in mind.

Engineers everywhere have been working to design earthquake-proof buildings, and it is hoped they are successful. One ingenious Russian contribution is a house built on springs to help absorb the shocks. Earthquake-wary Mexico City builds skyscrapers in sections on a rocker-like base. The only jarring note is that the proof will not come till *after* the next earthquake!

One reason why Anchorage snapped back to business as usual in short order was the aid given by nearby Elmendorf Air Force Base. A good part of the defense training there is preparing the men for action in case of enemy attack. The earthquake gave both civilians and military men a chance to practice what they had been drilling. It came without warning and was just as devastating as a full-scale bombing. The commander was pleased with the drill. His report said the base was able to give all-out help to the civilian population and still remain completely "combat o.k." It must have been frustrating to be unable to order retaliation against the enemy. But how do you strike back at an earthquake?

Alaskans did—in the only way they know. They dug in and worked, spent no time in self-pity, and kept a sense of humor. You might have to be an Alaskan to appreciate a sign that appeared on one of the shops on the main street that took the worst beating. Every spring there is much speculation as to the exact time the ice will break up. This massive breakup has a great bearing on how late some activities can be carried on and how early others can be started. It can be disastrous to miscalculate and end up somewhere in the middle. A giant pool is conducted and people bet on the exact time, down to the minute, when the breakup will come, the winner getting the cash. A sign on Mac's Foto Shop which collapsed and sank almost ten feet caused many a chuckle: "Closed due to early breakup."

Thinking of the long statehood struggle, some Alaskans feel that the earthquake discovery of Alaska had much publicity value—not all of it bad. It focused all eyes on Alaska and stimulated people to learn more about the state.

A homesteader for over twenty years on the Kenai Peninsula summed up: "At least everyone knows where we are now, and that we are a part of the United States."

A Continent Still in the Making

The state of Alaska is far from being completed, physically speaking. Evidence of this is constantly being sifted by scientists, geologists, geographers and geodetic surveyors. However, just plain people are also aware of certain changes, if they happen to be where they can observe or perhaps even be affected by them. They may be a captive audience in ringside seats for a spectacular show put on by nature. A show such as the Good Friday earthquake may be a real thriller and most frightening. However, survivors have a wonderful topic of conversation for years to

Smoking Pavlof volcano is on the tip of stormswept Alaska Peninsula; Aleutian Islands are hidden by distant clouds

come. They can hold an audience spellbound telling of "the time I saw the shape of a continent change."

These changes in greater and lesser degrees have been going on for millions of years. Alaska just happens to be located where there is still a lot going on. The difference is that once there are people to experience these phenomena, you hear about them. No doubt the rumblings and belchings of volcanoes as they awoke from time to time and the accompanying earthshaking and tidal waves were responsible for many native legends about spirits.

Only a little over fifty years ago, one of the greatest volcanic eruptions ever recorded rocked and changed the spectacular landscape of the Alaska Peninsula. One day this land had ice-capped peaks towering over a verdant green valley. Four days later mountains had been split open; the top of the tallest had been blown entirely away, leaving a two-mile wide crater. Some of the broadest, greenest valleys had been filled with one hundred to two hundred feet of molten sand.

The fireworks and repercussions were felt round the world. Hot ashes fell three feet deep on coastal Indian villages and covered Kodiak Island one hundred miles away with six inches or more. Smoke darkened this hemisphere for two days. Some of the ash, picked up by air currents, spread over the entire earth, lowering temperatures and making the atmosphere pink. It was four years before human beings could operate effectively in the area and study what happened.

Things had started popping June 2, 1912. Four days of increasingly severe earthquakes caused frightened natives to abandon the nearby village of Savanoski, never to return. Then a frothy foam of incandescent sand mixed with escaping gas welled up through fissures in the valley floor and surged at hurricane speed for fifteen miles downhill consuming glaciers, trees, and all living things in its path. Not actually a liquid, the glowing sand flowed on a cushion of gas.

After the sand-flow came the gigantic explosions, and towering mountains blew their tops, scattering ashes over the world. Eyewitnesses

Martin volcano in the Valley of Ten Thousand Smokes frequently erupts; tumbling ash scars the white glaciers on Mount Martin's flanks

who happened to be in boats in the vicinity had no choice but to wait out this awe-inspiring spectacle. Amazingly, the damage was limited to the landscape.

But the observers had no way of knowing that, and you can imagine how frightening nature's rampage must have been. For all they knew, the whole world was exploding. Though the ships headed for the open sea, a cloud of smoke and ashes kept pace. Dead and dying birds fell around them in the darkening pall and breathing was difficult. Many millions of fish were killed, apparently by underwater concussion or poisoning of the water by gases and acids. However, no one who went through the ordeal seemed to suffer any after effects.

The National Geographic Society was much interested in the area, and as soon as conditions permitted, they began a series of expeditions that continued several years. They discovered and named, appropriately then, the Valley of Ten Thousand Smokes, a fifteen-mile long valley with steam pouring from literally thousands of fissures. In 1918, a large area was named the Katmai National Monument. Since then it has been enlarged and is now the biggest Monument under National Park administration.

Visitors to the Valley of Ten Thousand Smokes find that its name no longer applies. The smokes have dwindled down to only a few. The sandflow is cut in some places by a hundred- and two hundred-feet deep minature Grand Canyons, where streams have eroded down to the pre-eruption ground level. It is a fascinating place to explore.

"We flew eighteen astronaut trainees into the Valley for landing practice not long ago," said airline representative Jim Dodson. "Its barren atmosphere, gullies, and slides of powdered pumice are the nearest thing on earth to what they can expect to find on the moon."

A rather startling impression of weightlessness is given by rocks floating in streams and lakes. Actually, these rocks are pumice, fused by the intense heat, and they are very light.

Glacier Bay National Monument, fifty air miles northwest of Juneau, is strikingly different from the Katmai, yet the two areas are amazingly similar in one respect. This is the creeping back of vegetation and other life after complete devastation; due to intense heat in one case, and in the other due to ice. Some places you see the beginnings of the cycle in the fungi. Others, the weeds, alpine flowers and lesser trees like alder and willow are making their contribution to the soil where some day there will be lush stands of spruce and hemlock.

Changes in Glacier Bay have been rapid in the last century as the glaciers have melted and retreated up inlets they themselves carved. These fjords are flanked by steep mountains, many of them perpetually snow-clad. Access to a fine new lodge is by boat and plane. From there a tour boat takes visitors to the face of mighty glaciers. The trip among icebergs is thrilling; a giant chunk falling off the glacier face is unforgettable. Other treats are spotting seal on the ice floes, watching huge whales blowing and porpoises playfully following the boat. High on sheer cliffs mountain goats pick their way, and black bear amble across shale slopes. Small islands are a bird-watcher's paradise with assorted waterfoul and even brilliantly-plumaged humming birds.

Both the Katmai and Glacier Bay Monuments provide intriguing on-the-spot laboratories. Teams of geologists and mining experts probe for minerals; one group is conducting a study on glaciers, including ice worms.

The land is violent enough all by itself; but recently the United States Government chose to give it a man-made shaking up for scientific study. Amchitka, a low treeless island in the Aleutians, was chosen for the blast which was set off in a deep hole drilled in the tundra. By analyzing seismic readings, scientists feel they can now tell the difference between underground nuclear explosions and natural earthquakes.

How Alaskans Put up with Their Unusual State

Everyday living in Alaska is a matter of adjusting to the peculiarities of that far north and westerly state. Alaskans who choose to live there are well aware that they may be up against problems that would never come up in other states. There are some conditions that can be classified as discomforts. A few could be called downright hazards. In between, a wide range of miscellaneous circumstances arise from time to time, to be endured as nuisances. Not that Alaska has a corner on such things; no spot is perfect. Many of the same hazards, discomforts, and nuisances are present in other states. But, as a rule, in Alaska, that same problem (like the state) will be bigger!

Mosquitoes are a good example. Control of a nuisance like this is very difficult in swamps and muskeg, and some parts of Alaska have little else. Some control of mosquitoes is maintained around big cities with modern methods of destruction of nearby breeding places. But fishermen, hikers, and hunters who persist in taking to the wilderness try all sorts of ways to defend themselves against these bloodthirsty pests.

The Indians naturally have an explanation for the mosquitoes in Alaska. Long ago there was a cannibal giant who lived on human blood. Since the giant had magic power, all arrows had no effect on him. He was apparently indestructible. But one valiant warrior learned that the giant had a vulnerable spot, his ankle. An arrow in the proper place would end the reign of terror. The warrior's arrow was true, and as the giant fell dying he had time to put a curse on the Indians and warn them that he would be back after their blood. According to their custom they built a huge fire to cremate his body and burned him down to ashes. In an effort to completely destroy him, they then scattered the ashes far and wide. Alas, the ashes turned into mosquitoes.

Anyone who is in Alaska during the mosquito season must wonder, along with the Indians, which is worse: having your blood gulped all at once or sipped in small, torturous bites.

On the whole, Alaskans fully expect certain conditions or a combination of them to exist at more or less predictable times and places. They prepare for them. They go even further and look on this business of living comfortably as a challenge, even a game, depending on the circumstances. Most important is the fact that there is rarely a situation so grim that someone doesn't see a funny side. A sense of humor is a real help in everyday living. At times, in Alaska it could be considered indispensable.

Take the subject of cold and all the related predicaments that can be caused by it. Generally speaking, cold would fit into the discomfort class, but in Alaska it is also somewhat of a nuisance. At times it can be a hazard. In the Interior, where temperatures drop in the winter to record-

Supplies are dropped to a marooned rescue plane on the Juneau Ice Cap

making lows, and in the Arctic regions, where the temperature never gets very high, people are accustomed to living with the cold.

Fairbanks, at the north end of the Alaska Highway, usually appears in the weather news in the dead of winter, especially when a cold snap with extremely low temperatures hangs on for a while, testing the endurance of the residents.

When the mercury dips to below − 50 ° and stays there for a month as it did one winter, there are problems in Fairbanks, second largest city in Alaska. Small planes are grounded, and even driving is hazardous because of an ice fog over the town. It is difficult to keep car engines running, plumbing freezes up, and it is a constant battle to keep both houses and people warm.

Keeping warm personally is a topic of conversation. Keeping covered is important; carelessly exposed hands, ears, and noses can become frostbitten in short order. People borrow ideas from their northern neighbors, the Eskimos. You see many warm, fur-lined parkas over wool pants, and mukluks for footgear. Even to run out just to start the car engine (necessary several times a day to keep it running in extreme cold) requires a full-scale bundling up.

Car owners make use of plug-in car heaters to keep engine blocks defrosted, and lug their batteries indoors at night. Tires have been known to harden into square shapes that could shatter like glass when the car starts moving. It is estimated that one year in Alaska equals four in the life of a car in any of the other states.

Not only cars suffered in one particularly severe winter. Correspondence from Alaskans near Fairbanks mentioned that furnaces and other machinery developed strange maladies, and that life seemed to be mostly a matter of surviving.

With their usual nonchalance toward the weather, however, people seem more interested than annoyed to have the subzero stretch last so long. They joke about maybe having outdoor ice hockey in July and agree that for sure they are having "five-dog weather." Translated, this means it would take two huskies at the foot of the bed and three across the middle to keep the sleeper warm. Everyone knows it is a cold night when a musher on a sled trail has to curl up with two or three of his dog team to keep warm!

A record low of − 84° is recorded for Snag, Alaska, a small town near the Canadian border. But no matter how low the lowest is reported, invariably some old sourdough will come up with the memory of a time when the mercury dropped still lower. One ninety-five-year-old declares he remembers when it was ninety-three degrees below zero when he was goldmining north of the Arctic Circle in Alaska in the 1890's.

Just as unbelievable and contradictory is the fact that temperatures in Fairbanks and surroundings are often recorded *above* 90° in the long, light summer!

Cold is responsible for another expensive nuisance. In areas where the ground is permanently frozen the roads are fine till the weather warms up in the spring. Then the surface thaws a few inches (or a few feet) causing black top to buckle under the strain or sink to give a roller-coaster effect to a highway. Unpaved roads may become as unstable as jelly in spots. Road maintenance is a perpetual problem, and it appears that road crews and heavy equipment will be forever a part of Alaskan scenery.

Permafrost, as this ever-frozen underground condition is called, made difficulties for miners who had to thaw the ground with fires to work their way down to remove and process what they hoped would be pay dirt.

Formerly if someone died in the winter, the body had to wait for a decent burial till spring, when the ground thawed. A popular small recreational building in one early-day town is still called The Morgue because of its previous use. In outlying Arctic towns today, there is often a small building standing in the cemetery, a stark reminder that at times it is necessary for people to compromise with their rugged land.

Alaskans who live in isolated or wilderness areas are well aware of hazards. In case of emergency or accident they are completely on their own, and whether they are able to survive depends on their stamina and resourcefulness. Though a trapper is familiar with his territory, there is always the chance of becoming lost in a sudden blizzard and having to wait out the weather. An unexpected dunking in a stream can be fatal unless a man knows how to build a fire and dry out in the next few minutes, or somehow keeps moving to prevent freezing into a solid chunk of ice. Even animals are potential hazards, perhaps not so much to his person as to his valuable food supply.

To protect the food from hungry and marauding animals small, sturdy wood cabins are built high off the ground. The cache is then stocked with staples. Meat, which keeps well in the cold, is added whenever the opportunity comes up. It is serious to run short, or have something happen to the food. It is a long way to the nearest supermarket. Caches are almost as much a symbol of Alaska as sled dogs, grizzled miners, and Eskimos.

Fire is a hazard even in large cities with the most modern fire-fighting equipment. Think what a fire meant to small, isolated Point Barrow, the village farthest north on this continent. Dogsleds had just brought oil drums in from the plane, and the three oil furnaces heating the largest building were being refueled when fire broke out. The town has no fire trucks or pumpers. Forty people had to get out in thirty-below weather.

The cache protects Alaskans' food from bears and other animals. The ladder is always moved away from the small door at the front

Firefighting equipment from a construction camp four miles away was unable to save the building, but kept the fire from spreading to the rest of the town. The loss was a real blow, for the building housed the Tundra Telephone Exchange, Miner's Bank, stores, warehouse, and a hotel.

A Long Supply Line

Because supplies must be imported from distant sources, many necessities are expensive in Alaska. Cost of living anywhere in the world is not a stable item. It may change from season to season, and there are many factors that influence whether it will be high, on a par with most other places or low. Visitors are more likely to notice prices. Residents become used to changes, and the wages adjust accordingly.

Alaska has the reputation of being high and this was true even in gold-rush days. If wanted items were available at all, they were so scarce as to be almost worth their weight in gold. A lot of gold dust exchanged hands to satisfy the cravings and thirsts of miners.

Today, the main reason for the higher living costs is still transportation. Satisfying the many needs of an ever-growing population is expensive, whether it is done by land, sea, or air. The costs are, as everywhere, passed on to the consumer. In the 1950's, figures showed that most things cost about half again as much in Alaska, with the figure correspondingly higher the more remote the community. Since then, the gap is probably lessening, as more efficient means of supply and packaging are used. Some reductions are made through home production or by reciprocal trade with foreign countries, principally Japan. However, it is likely that for some time to come Alaska will be dependent on obtaining her consumer goods from the Outside.

The cost of living seems of little concern to Alaskans, at least in the food department. Again, it gives them another chance to use their pioneer ingenuity, whether they live in a small town, big city or isolated homestead. Living off the land is a necessity in some cases and a help to the family economy in many others. All Alaskans would have a hard time denying that it isn't also a form of recreation.

Native people, especially, whose economy depends on combining the old and the new, still take off from jobs for seasonal hunting and fishing.

Rusty Lancashire kneads sourdough bread in her Kenai homestead kitchen

To a certain extent this practice gives natives the reputation of being unreliable in holding down jobs. It is possible this rumor was started by Alaskans in white-collar jobs who are jealous and wish they had thought of a similar good excuse for taking off during the hunting season. All Alaskans know that moose, caribou, bear, berries, fish stored in the locker or permafrost are the same as money in the bank.

Besides meat another essential food, bread, has a typical Alaskan flavor. The flavor is due to the sourdough base. Many Alaskan women prefer to bake their own bread, probably a carryover from the time when there was no place to buy it. Bread in the store is expensive; in many places it sells for as much as fifty-five cents a loaf.

The word sourdough has two meanings now. It describes a type of dough which can be used for all kinds of leavened baked or fried goods, including pancakes. It also means a grizzled old prospector who depended on it as an indispensable ingredient of his most conveniently carried staple food.

Sourdough starter was almost a miner's most precious possession. Yeast, sugar, and water are the components and they work, or come alive, at room temperature. Feeding the starter with flour and water keeps it alive and increases it to batter proportions. Enough is taken out for the day's use, and some is left in reserve as a start for the next batch. Since supplies were not easily available, the sourdough starter was carefully guarded. On the trail, the prospector even slept with it to keep the cold from destroying the organism. It would go on indefinitely under the right conditions, but if something happened to it, he had to beg, borrow, or steal another starter whenever he had the opportunity.

Usually there will be a crock for sourdough starter sitting on a kitchen shelf in Alaskan kitchens today. It may not be a necessity as it was in former years, but it is still the preferred basic ingredient for many baked goodies. Some Alaskans can boast that they are still using starter that was handed down to their family over forty years ago. After feeding watering, caring for, and using this simple, living organism for many years, sourdough starter probably seems like a member of the family, as much so as the family husky dog.

The Difference Between Work and Play

A crew-cut young Eskimo in a bright parka jumps on a giant walrus-hide blanket, held waist high above the ground by a ring of friends. As they cheer him on and flip the blanket, he starts to bounce: a few feet, ten feet, and finally as high as thirty feet in the air. Is he working or playing?

In this case he is playing, for he is competing in the thrilling Blanket Toss, one of the contests in the Eskimo Olympics, highlight of Fairbanks' annual midsummer Golden Days Festival.

But in decades past and for centuries, according to legend, this young man might have been performing the same activity, and called it *work*—important work. Traditionally, hunting parties used the Blanket Toss to spot distant game on endless flat tundra or ice floes, where it would be very hard to creep up on an animal without its being aware of the hunters first. The sharpest-eyed hunter in the bunch was tossed up to scan the surroundings for possible polar bears or spouting whales.

Performing the Blanket Toss is similar to working out on a trampoline, except that the jumper has help from a number of people. It requires a high degree of balance and coordination to stay upright; some become so adept that they can turn somersaults and still land on their feet. Sometimes the ground crew has to use some fancy footwork to keep under the jumper if he is inept or the wind gusty.

The Blanket Toss at the Eskimo Olympics in Fairbanks. Contestant may rise twenty feet!

At the beginning of the ceremonies, a breathless young athlete dressed in parka and mukluks sprints into the arena, holding aloft a flaming seal-oil torch. Amid the applause and cheers of the spectators, he lights the traditonal lamp with a flourish, and the Eskimo Olympic games are officially under way.

No one is fooled on the distance the runner has come; all Alaskans know that it was not far, or he would have been bogged down in tundra. And no one would have been surprised if he had landed by helicopter or plane. Most of the native contestants in the games and dances had to come that way from their remote arctic homes.

The formal welcoming speech is given first in Eskimo, then in English. Throughout, these Olympics follow the format of their ancient Greek counterpart, except that everything is pure Eskimo, and the background is unmistakably Alaska.

The contests are very old and based on developing the skills that have always been necessary for surviving in the Eskimo's harsh environment. As it is with many chores, making a game out of them and competing with one another made it more fun.

Besides the Blanket Toss there are many other games for developing strength, endurance, and agility. Such skills could mean the difference between life and death in a hand-to-fang struggle. A trained hunter could successfully leap a widening gap of frigid water should his ice floe suddenly break off from the rest. There are the Neck Pull, Finger Pull, Wrestling, and High Kick. In the Eskimo version of the High Kick, a sealskin is tied to a pole that is raised higher after every try, and *both* feet have to hit the skin at the same moment.

Visitors are invited to compete, too, and sometimes—to the delight of the crowd—someone from Outside will be brave enough to try. Unfortunately, it is risky for the inexperienced. A jet pilot and a newspaper man parted in good health at Anchorage. They met at Nome a day later to find they were both on crutches and wearing casts. Comparing notes, each had to admit he had tried the Blanket Toss in a bold moment.

There are a couple of contests, however, that have been left so far to the natives. One is the bloody sealskinning, a woman's contest. Only one tool is allowed, the *ooloo*, a curved, razor-sharp metal knife; and the winner completes the job in less than five minutes. The other is the muktuk-eating contest. You have to be Eskimo to eat whale blubber with gusto.

Between the physical feats, the spectators are entertained by groups of native dancers, competing for a trophy. Of course, there is a Queen Contest, and the attractive native girl reigns over the festivities wearing a striking parka and regal ermine crown.

When Is It Play Time in Alaska?

"Winter is fun time," most Alaskans will agree. At least, winter is the time when they feel they have the most time to play host to visitors from outside. Winter temperatures are more than offset by warmth of hospitality. Several major carnivals along with a large number of local community festivals are scheduled throughout the winter. Naturally, these celebrations are dictated by what they have the most of in winter—snow, and events are based on typically Alaskan pursuits. They feature skiing, marathon races, and that most popular pastime, sled-dog-racing.

These races are taken seriously and vary from day events to the world championship race held during the Anchorage Fur Rendezvous. The purse for the racers is more than seven thousand dollars for this three-day, seventy-five-mile endurance test. Spectators who manage to pick the winning musher may reap as much as five thousand dollars. Even children and women compete in special dogsled races, where the stakes may run over a thousand dollars.

The Anchorage Fur Rendezvous, held annually in February, is the highlight of the winter season. Besides the sled races there are all sorts of gay events, among them a Miners' and Trappers' Ball, native dancers, ski races at nearby Mount Alyeska, sports events like curling, sports car races, ice hockey, Eskimo Blanket Toss, art shows, concerts and Alaska's answer to the hamburger, mooseburgers. They also find time to auction off furs, which, after all, was the original purpose of the Rendezvous.

Baseball figures in special Alaskan treatment in two different celebrations. Snowshoe baseball is an unusual twist in Homer's Winter Carnival out on the tip of the Kenai Peninsula. And at the other extreme, mid-

End of seventy-five-mile dogsled race on the main street of Anchorage during the annual Fur Rendezvous

night sun baseball games are a feature of Fairbanks' Fourth of July entertainment.

These same activities are included in winter festivals held all over Alaska. The exception is the mild Southeast section, where water and woods are featured. But in each celebration there is always a colorful and unique local flavor added.

"Summer must be the time to play," claims someone vacationing in Alaska at that time of year.

Actually, what seems like play to him is one of many facets of Alaska's new and fast-growing big business, the tourist industry. Here the accent is on providing entertainment, recreational opportunities, and housing for a growing number of visitors.

74

Actually, *any* time is playtime; all that is needed is an excuse, even a small one. This happy-go-lucky attitude is evident from people to husky dogs. It takes a glimpse of only one small rabbit to send a whole working team off to the races.

Working in Alaska

In Alaska today, almost every kind of work found in the other forty-nine states will be going on somewhere. Most jobs, though not exclusive to Alaska because of the nature of the country, have a typical Alaskan twist. Many jobs tend to have a double role, depending on the participant's viewpoint. Take hunting and fishing, for example.

To an outsider, hunting and fishing in Alaska are a form of recreation. To some Alaskans, especially where big game abounds, hunting is a profession; guiding hunting and fishing parties is the way to earn a living. For the native population, hunting and fishing and storing up food for the winter is a basic necessity. For the head of an Alaskan family who perhaps works in an office hunting may be both recreation and a boost to his pay check. An Alaskan can probably count on bringing in from 250 to 500 pounds of moose meat for a half day's hunting. For some kinds of work, Alaska is unique. If you see a bearded character, complete with rifle and stalking a herd of caribou, don't jump to the conclusion that he is playing. He may be at work for the Wildlife Service, and the gun is for his protection.

Since the state is noted for tall mountains and vast wilderness inhabited by plentiful wildlife, jobs often follow outdoor recreational patterns. They sound like so much fun that these jobs are much sought after by college students, who may come from far places, though those attending the University of Alaska get first chance. Naturalists count and classify wildfowl in nesting grounds. Other workers count noses of assorted game and estimate size and migrating patterns of herds by air-plane over thousands of square miles of rangeland. Others study salmon-spawning streams and rivers, sometimes vying with bear over salmon netted for specimens.

Two college men spent one whole summer in isolation, marking off one-meter squares of tundra and counting and cataloguing every possible kind of vegetation therein that could be eaten as caribou food. Such surveys are necessary to determine the ratios of food and animals. How Alaska's natural resources, which seem so abundant in comparison with other states, are conserved will affect many aspects of both work and play in the future.

The military's cold-weather-training laboratory and survival school is near Fort Greely in interior Alaska. Here temperatures drop so low that plastics shatter at a touch, and even oil freezes solid. No play about this operation; the men are serious about learning how to survive in case they ever have to bail out of a plane over frozen tundra in the dead of winter.

Extremely hazardous are the floating ice-island laboratories used by scientists. When one will start to disintegrate and how fast is unpredictable. Even men based on more solid ground in the Arctic can get lost out in a sudden storm, or in the confusion of vast, unlandmarked whiteness.

Under somewhat more comfortable conditions, students at the University of Alaska study Alaska-orientated subjects and perform experiments aimed at making their state increasingly more livable. All efforts made by these pioneer workers may someday succeed in taming where necessary, but not changing, the character of the Northland.

What Is Woman's Work in Alaska?

Today's women are a far cry from some described in the poems of Robert W. Service: the "lady known as Lou" in the famous "Shooting of Dan McGrew," for example. There are a few left of the calibre of "Alaska Nellie" Lawing, who lived on the shores of Kenai Lake. During Alaska Railroad construction days this little slip of a woman was famed for her cooking at Mile 45 Roadhouse and for her dogsledding ability. Fellow Alaskans presented her with a gold nugget necklace and a citation praising the time she saved a life in a blizzard and mushed the mail through when strong men failed.

It is plain that women are indispensable in Alaska. They are also the

College students help Fish and Wildlife Service to band waterfowl, study lichen, and survey salmon migration

softening influence in a harsh land, just as pioneer women were in the West. They have advantages those women never dreamed of, not the least of which is education. The result is that Alaskan women lead busy, active lives with interests ranging from cultural projects to driving tractors, to politics. The image of a dreary, isolated existence that might have existed in the past is not true today.

Women are as vital, enthusiastic, and hearty in their play, as in their work. Generally, no distinction is made because of sex. Depending on their particular drives and interests they are adept and eager skiers, hikers, mountain climbers and dogsledders—and big game hunters, like Nina Whaley, a former "Miss Alaska!"

Nina, while an airline stewardess on a jet plane making trips into the Arctic, watched hunters come back with their trophies and decided to try it herself. She bagged her first one miles out on the ice: an eight-hundred-pound, eight-and-one-half-foot tall polar bear. Since then, she has added to her hope chest the skins of a grizzly and a black bear in other guided expeditions.

Men still outnumber women considerably, and a young single woman's chances for marriage and a career of homemaking are excellent.

"Alaska Nellie" Lawing was a renowned railroad construction camp cook and dogsled driver

L. F. Joy Elementary School is igloo-shaped to conserve heat in Fairbanks winters which reach 50° below zero

Men do have the edge in employment in seasonal jobs, like construction or fishing, for example. Women hold down the more stable, year-round jobs. Quite often working women are also wives and mothers, either because of economic necessity or because they are really needed in the labor market.

Thus, there are women clerks, secretaries, and bookkeepers in private and government offices. They adapt readily to communications jobs, including newspaper and radio work, and many find their niche in various kinds of transportation. Some pilot planes and helicopters. Others are airline stewardesses. Stewardess jobs are considered most interesting, because of Alaska's strategic location for world travel. It is not unusual for a stewardess to speak several languages or to be foreign-born.

Women are especially active in educational fields. Two excellent colleges—the University of Alaska at Fairbanks and Methodist University at Anchorage—offer opportunities for higher education. Statistics show that a majority of young women graduates have a degree in education, and they go on to make good use of it—in Alaska.

On the receiving end of the teaching profession are all the children of Alaska, whose principal work is becoming educated. All Alaskan children, white or native, between the ages of eight and sixteen years of age are expected to be in school. That was an important law passed in the meeting of the very first territorial legislature in 1913.

Going to School

It was hard to believe that the mercury had reached – 55 ° one day last January," said a Fairbanks mother. "Out in the school yard were fifteen or twenty youngsters merrily playing on swings and teeter-totters!"

She had driven her youngster to the L. F. Joy Elementary School rather than run the risk of having her wait twenty minutes or so for the school bus in the unusual, even for Interior Alaska, cold.

"Of course the children were all bundled to the eyes, with noses, ears and fingers warmly covered," the mother added. "The only identification might be a familiar cap or parka; otherwise they all looked like identical, little, chubby gnomes in various sizes."

The new and modern Joy School in Fairbanks is Alaska's answer to coping with the weather. The style has been described as Modern Igloo with a round gym and indoor playroom in the center and the classrooms circling the outside. A balcony swings around under the domed roof for the cafeteria and spectators. The central heating system efficiently heats the classrooms as well as the grates for stomping off snow at entrances, and a practical parka-drying room.

In cities, at least, everyday things like school go on much as they do in other states. Schools compare very favorably both in physical construction and philosophy. They are integrated and for all, regardless of background. Besides institutions of higher learning in the two largest cities, there are locally formed community colleges in the smaller ones.

Religious groups as well as the Federal government have had a hand in seeing that education is possible in small villages. Since 1884 the Alaska Native Service under the Department of Interior has assumed responsibility for native education and recruitment of teachers. Recently established vocational and art schools for natives at Nome and Haines-Port Chilkoot are the concern of both the state and Federal government.

The solons who passed the compulsory school attendance law in 1913 really meant it. A variety of schools is available, but if it should happen that a family lives where it is impossible to attend regular school, there is always the correspondence school. Many a homesteading family has successfully fulfilled Alaskan educational requirements by mail.

Typical Work in Southeast Alaska

The cities of Southeast Alaska owe their existence to natural resources for which they are noted, mainly from the forests and sea. They are alike in climate, with mild temperatures and rain, similar to the coastal cities of the Pacific Northwest. A cross section of much of the typical work being done in Alaska today can be found in and around the cities of Ketchikan, Wrangell, Petersburg, Sitka, Juneau, Haines-Port Chilkoot and Skagway.

The newest way to visit these cities is by ferry. Pride and joy of Southeastern Alaskans, the new Alaska State Ferry system, has broken the isolation barrier, which till recent years held them back and kept them from feeling a part of the rest of Alaska.

Ketchikan stretches along steep hills on the Inside Passage. Indian name for town means "wings of spread eagle"

Suppose we join a cruise of the *Malaspina* flagship of the ferry fleet, as it stops first at Ketchikan and then continues up the Inside Passage. Though these towns are similar in many physical ways, we will see that each has kept its own distinctive, individual flavor and typical occupations.

Ketchikan — Salmon Capital of the World

Ketchikan—more sneeze than name—was probably derived from the Indians. Their words "Kach Khanna" are translated "spread wings of prostrate eagle." The town fits that description when seen from the air. It is built on a precipitous site, with little room between the water and mountain backdrop. So it has spread along the waterfront for about five miles, but is only a few hundred yards deep.

One mountain interferes with the main street itself, right in the center of town. Engineers solved this problem with a tunnel. Half of the thoroughfare goes through, the other half goes around this otherwise insurmountable obstacle. One way traffic each way, of course.

Long the custom in Indian villages, open-air Indian art displays are still a fascinating feature of Ketchikan. To the south end is Saxman Indian village and to the north is Totem Bight. Both places have well-kept totem pole displays, and at Totem Bight there is a reproduction of an Indian community house as well.

Ketchikan is a city of six or seven thousand population. It has good schools, attractive homes, a fine new hospital, healthy industries and constantly improving business facilities. These, along with skyscraper apartments, hotels and completely stocked stores, make the town eligible to be called modern. Principal industries are pulp, logging, and fishing. A giant modern pulp mill, an up-to-date sawmill, and canneries are mainstays of the town's economy.

Though salmon as a source of income has been topped by wood pulp, the residents are proudest of the fishing. They claim the title Salmon Capital of the World. And salmon are everywhere! In late summer, spawning salmon, returning to lay their eggs in the river of their origin, jump a rapids in a river that rampages right through town. The patriarch of all Salmon Derbies runs from March 15 to July 15, with weekly prizes awarded. A record salmon was over a hundred pounds. However, it is not unusual to hear a fisherman (perhaps a tourist) brag that he hooked one or two forty-pound salmon in a couple of hours.

The same rain that keeps the forests flourishing falls on people, too. Ketchikan residents are resigned to their weather, noted for its extremely heavy rainfall, an average of 154 inches a year. Everyone expects it, dresses for it, and can even make jokes about it. As the rain capital of the United States, bets are made on extent of total rainfall with the closest guess winning the pool (money, not more water). With so much rain, the town has a freshly laundered feel and there are few places in the United States as lush and green. When rain clouds lift, so do spirits. In contrast, nothing is so rare as a sunny day in Ketchikan: rare in the sense of bright blue sky, sparkling water, and fresh clean-washed air.

Wrangell — Canning and Export Center

Next ferry port of call is Wrangell, also on an island, ninety miles to the north of Ketchikan, a little over six hours by ferry. Though there is no lack of mountains in the distance, this town is situated on comparatively flat land instead of the usual precarious perch of other southeast Alaska cities. Its population is about fifteen hundred and its main industries are freezing and canning seafood: salmon, shrimp, crab, and halibut. Wrangell claims to be the leading export city of Alaska mainly because of its lumber shipments to Japan. Almost any day there will be a ship in the harbor displaying the Japanese flag, an oriental name, and taking on a load of Alaskan timber from the big Japanese-owned sawmill.

Wrangell has a most interesting history; it has changed flags and names three times in a little over a hundred years. In 1833 it was a Russian fort. For a while the Russians leased the fort to the British. Finally in 1867 the United States bought it from Russia along with the rest of Alaska.

Wrangell's strategic location on the Stikine River made it an important supply depot for both fur traders and gold seekers. Today, in summer visitors can retrace the historic gold route by big riverboat, which

Giant king crab are trapped in seven-foot crab pots in windy Aleutian Islands

makes the four-day, one-hundred-sixty-three-mile round trip to Telegraph Creek in British Columbia, Canada, once a week.

Only a short walk from downtown a footbridge leads to a tiny island where there is a fine collection of restored Tlingit totem poles and a chief's tribal house. A delightful park, Chief Shakes Island, is also a gathering place for townspeople. In the summer, when the tide of the warm Japanese current comes in over the flats, Indian and white youngsters splash together happily, while their parents watch and visit on the grassy lawn surrounded by totem poles.

Petersburg — Little Norway

It takes a little more than three hours for the ferry to wind north up the famous Wrangell Narrows between Kupreanof Island and Mitkof Island to the site of Petersburg. At some points the ship, the size of a small ocean-liner, seems to fill the channel.

"If my arms were a few inches longer, I could add that pretty shell on the beach to my collection," a passenger might remark. Deer are easily spotted along the shore.

84

The small town with a population of about fifteen hundred is in a lovely setting of snow-capped mountains and fjords, and is called Little Norway. The scenery helps to inspire this label. However, the whole character of the town smacks of Scandinavian thrift and neatness. Scandinavian accents are evident in conversations with friendly townspeople.

Petersburg has none of the violent and lawless reputation to the shame of other Alaskan cities in certain periods of history. Instead of stampeding for gold in 1898, the Scandinavian settlers were hard at work building neat white houses and pursuing their age-old occupations of fishing and lumbering.

Today, some of the third generation of these pioneers work in a dozen logging camps to harvest one hundred million board feet of timber a year. The others gather and process twenty million pounds of seafood; a particularly tiny, tasty shrimp is a Petersburg specialty. The area also is famous for big game hunting, and they claim the world record salmon—one hundred twenty-six and one-half pounds.

Fishing boat takes on freshwater ice from glacial iceberg. Many students have summer jobs with the fleet

But it is not all work and no play. One of their big celebrations naturally, is Norwegian Independence Day, the Seventeenth of May. The traditional smorgasbord of Scandinavian specialties becomes a gastronomical challenge when every favorite Alaskan delicacy is added to the groaning tables. It takes at least three days to polish off the feast, and that is how long the festivities last. Happy townspeople and guests don native costumes of the old country and untiringly dance the polka and the schottische.

Sitka — From Fur Trading to Wood Pulp

Three times a week the ferries deviate from their direct route north up the Inside Passage and make a side trip to the outside seaport of Sitka. Though isolated now in comparison with other Southeast Alaska cities daily connected by ferry, for half a century Sitka was the most important city in Alaska. Under the iron-handed administration of the Russian Governor Baranof, it grew and prospered as a leading fur-trading center. Even after the transfer to the United States in ceremonies held at Sitka in 1867, it remained the seat of government till the capital was moved to Juneau in 1906.

Sitka is situated on Baranof Island in a large archipelago, a group of offshore islands considered to have a common origin. In this case, the islands are related in that they are the exposed tops of an extensive submerged coastal mountain range. This is the impression when the area is seen from the air, and the feeling of sailing among mountain tops is even more pronounced as the ferry carefully picks its way through the maze during its six-hour journey to Sitka. The route is so tricky in spots that a ferry now and then scrapes bottom when time and tide are incorrectly estimated.

A high point in this collection of islands is snow-capped Mount Edgecumbe, a nearly perfect volcanic cone that Sitkans say resembles Mount Fuji in Japan. Mount Edgecumbe dominates the scenery, and the rest of the islands look like scattered jewels, green and flourishing in their sea-blue setting.

Early in 1966 a fire at Sitka destroyed half of the business district and one of the most charming tangible pieces of evidence of Russian occupation. For well over one hundred years in the very center of town stood the Cathedral of Saint Michael, a Russian Orthodox church built in 1844 and still used. Its original log structure had been covered over with boards and painted, but looking down the main street, which had to divide and go on each side of the church, the visitor recognized the unmistakable lines of Russian architecture in the tall spire of the onion dome bell tower.

Visitors were welcome at specified times and the guide might be a priest or the bishop himself in his flowing black robes—his gentle, dignified bearded face under the square black headgear and in his hand his staff of office. As soon as you stepped over the threshold, well-worn by the faithful over the century, a feeling of reverence and then awe at the beauty of the interior were overwhelming. The plaster walls and stark furnishings were forgotten as you looked at the priceless religious art objects. A mural of "The Last Supper" was above the altar. A lovely madonna and child portrayed in gold, silver, precious jewels, and oils adorned another wall. There were an ancient pipe organ; chimes from Moscow, laboriously brought across the Siberian Steppes; and rich embroideries, carvings, chalices and other trappings of religious significance.

Despite the fire almost everything inside was saved, and plans were started immediately for rebuilding the church, just as it was before. Funds to do this were offered the next day by the Moquawkie Indian tribe, who have struck it rich in oil fifty miles south of Anchorage, and by others saddened by loss.

Some mementoes of the past in Sitka and vicinity are reminders of bloody battles fought between the Russians and natives. Today on the site of the first fort and of one of the most violent clashes there is the Sitka National Monument, a collection of many finely carved towering totems. Some day on recently discovered foundations there may be a reconstruction of the old Indian fort, which the Russians burned in 1804.

The violence is all in the past. Sitka, like many other Alaskan cities, has her hands full with the present and future growth of her industries and population.

One recent important boost to Sitka's economy is a large pulp plant, built and owned by Japan. Perhaps the Japanese chose Sitka for this business site because of the resemblance to their homeland, complete with Fuji-like mountain. At any rate, the mill consumes considerable Alaskan timber for products shipped to Japan and other parts of the world.

Schools are well established at Sitka, including the Mount Edgecumbe Alaska Native Service School, and Hospital and the Sheldon Jackson Junior College, one of the first schools in the Territory of Alaska. The Alaska Pioneers Home is right in the center of town on the former parade grounds of Russian and American troops. A fully equipped, modern hospital and well-established businesses all add to Sitka's stable economy.

However, there are problems of growth. What to do with increasing population will be in a process of solution for a long time to come.

Original St. Michael's Cathedral at Sitka was built in 1844 during Russian rule. Priceless art objects saved from 1966 fire will be housed in rebuilt church

Permanent new homes are being built in subdivided areas, with all the necessary planning of streets and sewers. Traffic is a problem now with the influx of cars on winding city streets. Some streets date from Russian days, when they were meant only for foot traffic.

Meanwhile, people of Sitka are proud of the many firsts in their history, including being the first capital of Alaska. Every year they hold their Alaska Day Celebration. Then the whole town turns out in early Russian and American garb, to reenact the actual ceremony of the transfer of Sitka to the United States in 1867—from the sale to the signing.

Juneau — Gold and Government

Juneau is the first southeastern Alaska city visited by the northbound ferry that is not on an island. But it might as well be. There are no roads leading over a most formidable mountain and glacier barrier into the Interior, and no likelihood of one being constructed in the near future. The Marine Highway links the capital with the rest of Alaska and so does a constant flow of air traffic, including jets at the large Municipal Airport and various-sized seaplanes at the city docks.

A first impression of the city itself is that there really is not room for a city; long fjords on one side and precipitous mountains on the other hem it in. The airport had to be made longer for jet landings by dredging earth from a nearby bay. Then why did a city get started in such an illogical setting? The answer, of course, was gold.

In 1880 two prospectors, outfitted at Sitka, headed up Gastineau Channel and discovered one of the richest gold strikes of all time. Their names were Joe Juneau and Dick Harris, and they were soon followed by other gold seekers—enough to start a town, first named Harrisburg and later changed to Juneau. There was not the bonanza growth or wild gold fever that accompanied later strikes. Neither did the strike at Juneau fizzle out as it did in other boom towns. Juneau grew and prospered gradually as mining developed on a large scale.

The Alaska-Juneau Gold Mine, a landmark against the steep mountainside, prospered till 1944, when the cost of mining the gold overtook the selling price, and it had to shut down. The gold supply is by no means exhausted, but overhead costs absorb the profit.

However, the mine was reopened recently for a different purpose. Visitors, after watching a costumed skit about early-day life in Juneau, can take a short excursion on an ore train through old mine buildings to a viewpoint above the city.

"Some people think Juneau is too isolated and too far from the center of Alaska to be the capital," remarks a Juneau resident.

He is likely to continue with the argument that it is just as logical to complain that Washington, D.C., should not be the capital of the United States because of its far-from-central location. At any rate, since the capital was moved from Sitka, the issue has been up for discussion—and two votes by the population. So far Juneau is the winner, and her isolation seems to be no particular deterrent to the transaction of government business. Moreover, with tourism and government becoming big industries along with lumber and fish, Juneau has more than held its own economically.

Southeast Alaska is called the banana belt because of its mild year-round climate. Juneau's weather refutes the snow and ice conception of Alaska. This is all the more surprising because the town is situated almost underneath a large ice mass—the Juneau Icefield, made up of over a thousand square miles of glaciers which extend all the way into Canada. This ice cap is fascinating to scientists and for twenty years has served as a most accessible laboratory. By plane and helicopter, well-supplied expeditions take off to perform their scientific duties, knowing that, unlike expeditions to the North Pole, they are within easy return to metropolitan Juneau with all its comforts.

Juneau's Neighborhood Glacier

One of the glaciers having its source in the Juneau Icefield is the huge Mendenhall, unique among glaciers because people can drive right up to it all year long. It extends almost to Juneau's backyard. One of the few glaciers anyone can look right in the face, the Mendenhall is a tourist attraction as well as the object of much scientific research.

The new Visitor Center is built on rocks exposed only in the last twenty-five years. A short trail leads to a viewpoint just across the small

Mendenhall Glacier is two miles wide and twelve miles long. It extends from over a mile high on Juneau Icecap to practically sea level

lake in front of the icy face. The ice wall is one hundred to two hundred feet high in places and one and one-half miles wide. As you watch, chunks—some of them house size—break off and fall in the lake, causing a small tidal wave with sound effects. The ice you now see fell as snow perhaps two hundred years ago fourteen miles up in the Juneau Icefield at about four thousand feet elevation. It is a most heavenly shade of blue: on dull days the color is most intense, deeper than skyblue velvet with a frosty nap.

The Mendenhall is an example of a receding glacier, which means that the ice is melting faster than it is moving forward, causing the ice face to retreat slowly. Sometime in the 1700's scientists figure it made a maximum advance and reached a point about two miles from its present face. And so the estimated movement forward of a few inches to about five feet per day is not enough to prevent it from backsliding about ninety feet a year.

Though the glacier itself is the main attraction, the surrounding terrain provides a fascinating study in contrasts. In these contrasts are clues which help scientists determine the effects on human, plant, and animal life and what might be expected in the future.

Around the sterile glacier face are found sparse lichens typical of those found in arctic wilderness hundreds of miles to the north. In adjacent valleys and mountain slopes are the dense vegetation and rain forests. The moderate, moist climate and long summer days encourage a prolific growth of wild flowers. Yellow skunk cabbage, magenta fireweed, purple lupine, and Alaska's state flower—the blue forget-me-not—are predominating varieties.

A network of roads, including a paved modern highway leading to the glacier, seems surprising when the only way to other parts of Alaska by car is by way of the Marine Highway. But fine recreation areas and points of interest in the vicinity of Juneau justify them. Though Juneau has more miles of roads than her sister Southeast Alaska cities, they all have their local roads and parking meters and an amazing number of vehicles using them.

In Juneau, as in all Alaskan cities, the past is very close to the present, and evidence abounds. In this case a large amount of it has been handily corralled in the very fine State Museum. Curator of the museum until his retirement recently was Edward Keithahn, an outstanding authority on Indian totems and other Alaskan art and historical subjects. Browsing among the well-kept and classified cases, a visitor will discover many imagination-stirring mementoes of Russian occupation or gold-rush frenzy. Here, too, are found some of the rarest and finest examples of Indian and Eskimo art and culture—priceless treasures.

Within a few blocks of the museum are other reminders of the past. An outstanding totem pole stands next to the Governor's stately mansion. Nearby, almost hidden by other, newer buildings, is a small Russian Orthodox church, with typical onion-dome architecture.

Since space is at a premium, the only way to grow—as in many cities in other states—is in the suburbs. Twelve miles from Juneau on flats formerly occupied by the Mendenhall Glacier new homes, schools, and other necessary facilities are being built.

"I'll take a chance on what those science fellows say—the Mendenhall won't be back this way for quite a while," declares one enthusiastic home builder. "And just look at that view!"

Haines and Port Chilkoot — Tourist Ports

The Marine Highway officially ends where it first connects with a road leading to the Alaska Highway, and thus to other parts of Alaska. Bits and pieces of this ferryboat highway continue on at northern roadends to serve cities on islands and peninsulas in the Gulf of Alaska to the west.

The northern terminal of the Marine Highway is unusual in that it ends at *two* small cities, Haines and Port Chilkoot, situated in a spectacular fjord-like setting near the end of Lynn Canal. They are surrounded by snow-capped peaks plunging into glacial blue-green waters. It is the best scenery reached by ferry or car and a rewarding climax to the ferry trip. The towns are like Siamese twins as they lie side by side, but otherwise they are quite separate and different in character.

Haines was founded in 1890 as a Presbyterian mission. Its growth soon tied in with the discovery of gold in the Klondike. The town became important as a point of entry to the gold diggings, as did Valdez, Nome, and Skagway. The Dalton Trail was the famous one passing through Haines, and the town saw its share of gold seekers. Discovery of gold in 1900 in the Porcupine area, only thirty-six miles from Haines, prompted further growth. Haines's less violent reputation during peak gold-rush times was due, perhaps, to the religious influence.

Haines is the business area for Port Chilkoot. Stores, banks, schools, and churches for both towns are mainly at Haines. Tourist facilities are found in both. The general appearance of Haines is neat and conventional, leaning toward frontier-type buildings. However, with periodic face-lifting going on and an upward curve in the economy, the pioneer look will no doubt fade away.

The economy of both towns has been boosted by several industries: mining, fishing, lumbering, oil storage, and transportation. And, of course, tourism. Visitors knew Haines from tour ships that stopped there, and car travelers in summer would wander down the 159-mile cutoff from the main Alaska Highway. But the biggest boost to the towns was the opening of the Marine Highway and year-round maintenance of the

Haines Highway. This made Haines and Port Chilkoot the gateway of the shortest water-land route to the Interior of Alaska.

Skagway — Frontier Town

Skagway, a mere seventeen-mile side trip by ferry beyond Haines, is an alternate terminal for the Marine Highway. In 1898 the historic city had a population of twenty thousand, and was the jumping-off place for the Trail of '98 to the Klondike goldfields. It does not connect with the rest of Alaska by road, but by an historic narrow-gauge railroad. By 1900 the White Pass and Yukon Railroad had blasted its way up the precipices side by side with the stampeders. This would be a tricky maneuver today; it was a fantastic engineering feat in those early days, with only pick and shovel and scraper.

Now, instead of laboriously hiking over the famous Chilkoot Pass as thousands of heavily-laden gold seekers did, travelers can ship themselves and car over the Trail of '98 via parlor car and flat car. It is a 111-mile trek into history that ends at the town of Whitehorse, Yukon Territory, Canada. From Whitehorse, the traveler can go on to Alaska by way of the Alaska Highway.

Some rugged people hike the trail every once in a while, just to get the feel of history. But from the train and in comfort, it is possible to get a good enough idea how extremely difficult those trails were. The gold-crazed hikers *could* have been warned by an Indian legend.

The name Skagway is derived from the native word *Skagua,* which when translated means "the home of the North Wind." The Indians held that when white men crossed the summit of the pass, a chinook (a suddenly warm wind) would melt the snow and cause a terrible avalanche. On the basis of this word from their spirits, they jealously guarded the pass from use by white men, while at the same time profited by being the exclusive traders with Interior natives.

A chinook did melt the snow at the height of the migration of white men toiling over the trail in thousands. The ensuing avalanche—tons of heavy, wet snow—engulfed the route, killing and injuring many.

Skagway's population has dwindled to about seven hundred now. At first glance visitors wonder what keeps the town going. They soon realize

Skagway, lively ghost town, is at the end of the Inside Passage. It is the Terminus of the Trail of '98

that, as an entry point to Canada and on north to Alaska, it provides the important seaport terminus for the White Pass and Yukon Railroad.

The new ferry system is bringing more tourists to Skagway. The residents are beginning to recognize the potential in this new, developing industry. They also realize that the charm of Skagway lies in its link with the past. Townspeople may work at other jobs, but a great community effort is directed at keeping the town much as it was in Days of '98.

There are the weather-beaten, square, false-fronted buildings that mark a frontier town. Boardwalks have not yet given way to paved sidewalks. The historic Golden North Hotel has rooms decorated in the original furnishings of the day. Citizens of Skagway have combed the town for historic materials and mementoes, with the result that a wealth of antiques and historical items is preserved. The Trail of '98 Museum is housed in the first granite building built in Alaska. Just for fun, townspeople dress up and reenact gold-rush highlights, like "The Shooting of Dan McGrew" to keep the gold-rush atmosphere alive.

Skagway is a town that grows on you. It looks like a ghost town, but feels very much alive. The ghosts are there, though, you feel as you wander down the main street imagining what it was like in 1900 with twenty thousand peple milling around.

As you look back over the ferry route from the end of the line at Skagway, it is evident that all Southeast Alaska communities have two natural resources in common: water and trees. Lots of water spurs the rapid growth and regrowth of lots of trees, the raw material providing jobs in all phases of the lumber industry, from logging to pulp manufacture.

Logging in Alaska

Logging is considered rugged men's work any place, especially out West where the trees grow big. The trees may be no bigger, but there are other problems in harvesting Alaskan forests of western hemlock, Sitka spruce, and cedar. The land is bigger, wilder, and wetter. Logging is expensive because of transportation problems and distances from markets and sources of necessary equipment.

However, one thing that helps to make up for the high cost of logging and transportation of products is the proximity of logs to water. About 90 percent of usable timber in Southeastern Alaska is within three miles of tide water, and the timberline is only about fifteen hundred feet in elevation.

"Logging here can be compared to logging on Puget Sound, Washington, about one hundred years ago," a spokesman for the Alaska Loggers' Association states. "When logging companies in Washington were opening up the territory, they were operating near tidewater. Shiploads of poles were being rolled directly into Puget Sound to become masts for square-riggers."

The similarity to the past ends there, for Alaskans make use of the most modern machinery and methods available, no matter what they cost or how difficult it may be to obtain them. They have also had to invent equipment on the spot as the need arose.

A most fascinating Alaskan innovation is the floating A-frame—a giant derrick-like structure on a raft or barge. Powered by big diesel engines, it tows the logs directly off the hillsides to where they splash into tidewater.

A-frame operations are common with both big companies and small. Often there will be a nearly floating logging camp—either a tiny village of houseboats or a converted landing-ship bunkhouse for bachelor loggers.

Another striking example of Alaskan ingenuity is adapting often-used big winches, called yarders, and derricks or loaders to rough Alaska terrain by mounting them on top of World War II medium-sized tanks.

Free enterprise and the typical rugged individualism of Alaskans makes it possible for independent *gyppo* logging companies (sometimes five men or fewer) to work shoulder to shoulder with the two big pulp companies in Southeast Alaska. The small companies are loosely tied together for their own interest with membership in the Alaska Loggers' Association. Through the Association they exchange ideas on mutual problems, keep abreast of legislation that would affect them, promote their own safety program and generally keep in touch with one another. The Association's central office in Ketchikan offers them two-way radio service, runs an informal employment bureau, and may even put in the grocery order for the small-camp cook.

"Thick as hair on the back of a dog" is the way the "Old Settler's Song" describes the trees of the Pacific Northwest in early days. This description certainly still fits the islands among which the ferry passes. Not even a logging road mars the scenery.

How long will the supply of timber last? Though demands are growing and trade is expanding to foreign countries, principally Japan, it appears that there will be logs for some time in Alaska. Nature provides ideal conditions of mild, wet climate for replenishing the forests. Regrowth is rapid on logged slopes. Even so, Alaskans in logging and allied industries intend to profit by any mistakes made by pioneer loggers in other states. They are keeping a wary, evaluating eye on this important and valuable Southeast Alaska resource.

From Russian America to Statehood

In 1867, the United States was given first chance to buy a sizeable piece of real estate. The price was right; in fact, a bargain. The price tag on all Russia's holdings in what was then known as Russian America was a mere $7,200,000. Sounds like a lot of money? It divides out to a cheap two cents an acre.

The United States, through the considerable effort of the Secretary of State, William Seward, was given the option to buy. After three weeks of negotiation, Seward and the Russian Minister to the United States had a treaty ready. All that remained to complete the sale was to sign this treaty, to take it to the Senate to be ratified, and to make appropriations for paying Russia for the land. The last two items turned out to be a monumental task.

"To buy or not to buy" was the basis for heated debates in a special session of the Senate, called for deciding the issue. Part of the trouble was the apparent haste throughout the handling of the matter. It made people suspicious. No matter that Seward thought the purchase a wonderful bargain and one which would prove to be of great value in the years to come. As is often the case, the farsightedness of the man was to go unrecognized until many years after his death.

It worried solons and public alike that the very next day after the treaty was drawn up Seward was insisting on signatures—and at four

Governor's mansion at Juneau has authentic Indian totem pole

o'clock in the morning! Then there was the rush to the capitol and the insistence on a special session. What proof was there that Russia was not trying to unload a white elephant on us?

One lawmaker commented, "Russia is trying to sell us a sucked orange." He was obviously thinking of the plunder of furs under Russian occupation.

Some prominent leaders referred to Alaska as being of absolutely no value, even calling the proposed sale an outright swindle. One Eastern representative called Alaska "a barren, unproductive region, covered with ice and snow." Another went even further to say that anyone who would leave the United States to seek a home in such a place must be insane.

Many derisive names were applied to Russian America. One was *Walrussia,* of course. Others were Seward's Icebox (no automatic refrigerators in those days!) and Seward's Folly, *Polaria, Icebergia,* American Siberia, and Zero Islands. To this day, Alaska is trying to live down some of the false impressions started by those old, bitter debates.

That the purchase of Alaska became such a political issue was also due to the political unrest at the time. It was soon after the Civil War, tempers were still on edge, and President Andrew Johnson was having domestic problems. In fact, he was facing impeachment. A real estate deal being hurried through was bound to be snapped up by the opposition as another case of political graft.

There were many who heartily agreed with Seward, as well as those who were willing to listen with open minds to arguments on both sides. Actually, Russia's motives were friendly. Relations between the two countries had always been good. However, she was of the opinion that it was only a matter of time before either the United States or Great Britain would take over Alaska anyway.

Russia preferred the United States. It is possible that she considered selling leased land out from under their feet an excellent way to annoy the British. At any rate, Russia had discovered it was quite a job to administer her distant colonies, and she needed money. It is most likely that Russia signed the treaty with the sincere wish to do a favor for the

United States. In which case, it would have seemed ungrateful and poor public relations to turn it down.

Whatever the reasons on both sides, time has shown that it was more Moscow's Folly than Seward's Folly. If it had not been for the determination of Seward and the eloquence of Senator Charles Sumner of Massachusetts, the sale might have fallen through. If it had, the history of Alaska, as well as that of the rest of the United States, might have taken a very different course.

The final clincher for the sale was a masterful job of oratory by Senator Sumner. Though he was no special friend of Seward, politically, and had compunctions about acquiring the territory without consulting the inhabitants, he became convinced that the purchase was in the best interests of the United States. He made a thorough study of everything then known about Russian America and eloquently summed it all up in a three-hour speech before the Senate. Much of it convincingly questioned the view that the territory was worthless and pointed out its great potential. In conclusion he suggested the name *Alaska*.

When the vote was cast, the decision was favorable but with only one vote to spare. In those days there were forty-five members in the Senate. With everyone present, thirty favorable votes would be needed to give the required two thirds for ratification. On that day six were absent and the vote was twenty-seven for, twelve against. Someone suggested that they make the vote unanimous, but they did not quite make it. The final vote on the official record stood at thirty-seven to two.

On such a narrow margin rested the fate of Alaska. The purchase put an end to all foreign exploration and marked the beginning of her history under the sovereignty of the United States.

Centennial Year

Suppose we choose one day out of Alaska's first year of history, 1867. It might as well be an important one: October 18, the day that the formal ceremonies were held transferring Russian America, renamed Alaska, from Russia to the United States. The place was Sitka, the capital and center of culture. The time was the middle of the afternoon, described as quiet and misty by one poetic historian, but clear and beautiful in the official United States report of the proceedings. The harbor at Sitka, with its unusual number of ships awaiting the ceremonies, made an impressive backdrop of green forest, mountains, and sparkling water.

A hundred Russian troops and nearly two hundred American soldiers, sailors, and marines marched up Baranof Hill and lined up in front of the Governor's house. The Russian flag still dipped with the light breeze from the top of the ninety-foot flagpole. Perhaps sixty American civilians were present but only a handful of Russians, who were sorry to see the end of their era in the gay capital. Brigadier-General Lovell H. Rousseau and several officers in full-dress uniform stood at attention on behalf of the United States. Russia was represented by Prince Dimitrii Maksutov —the Governor—and Captain Aleksei Peschurov. The men were bearded and the ladies bonneted in the fashion of the day.

Brief, appropriate speeches were cordially exchanged by the Governor and the General. Gun salutes were fired alternately by Russian and American ships. Then, as Princess Maksutova, lovely wife of the Governor wept, a Russian sailor lowered the double-eagle ensign of Imperial Russia. General Rousseau's private secretary stepped forward and hoisted the Stars and Stripes of the United States in its place.

Now let's lower the curtain on this tableau (as they do in plays) to denote the passage of time: a hundred years to be exact. The curtain rises, and the date is October 18, *1967*.

But the scene is the same! The Governor and his Princess; the General; the uniformed troops; the flagpole; the onlookers, bearded and bonneted; the gun salutes . . .

However, looking beyond the immediate action, we know that this is a reenactment of that important event. These are actors in a play, whose garb contrasts sharply with the spectators wearing modern dress. And the setting will vary, depending on where the traveling group of players happens to be presenting the pageant. In Fairbanks there will be a contrasting backdrop of modern skyscrapers dwarfing modest gold-rush-built log cabins. Anchorage, streamlined and modern, would have little outside of the action on stage to remind one of those historic days.

Painting of the flag raising at Sitka, October 18, 1867, during ceremonies transferring Alaska from Russia to the United States

Smaller towns, some of which have changed little in appearance since early days will capitalize on this, even searching through old trunks for costumes of early days. It might be hard to tell which are actors and which townspeople in places like Sitka and Skagway.

Alaska has a large choice of important dates to celebrate during its Centennial year. March 30 is Seward Day, set aside to honor William Henry Seward for his foresight instead of his folly. Alaskans who know how to give a party as well as enjoy one are not likely to pass up any opportunities for celebrating.

There are almost unlimited important events to be singled out and celebrated: discovery of gold, discovery of Alaska, opening of the Alaska Highway or the railroad or the new State Ferry, founding of the

103

Sitka has a fine harbor. Mount Edgecumbe, a nearly perfect volcanic cone, is on the right

first permanent settlement, meeting of the first legislature. Conveniently, both the University of Alaska and McKinley National Park celebrate fiftieth anniversaries in 1967; the Alaska Methodist University, its tenth.

With typical hospitality the invitations to the Centennial party include everyone interested, from Russian representatives (through the State Department) to tourists from Outside, all over the world. Pure coincidence that, barring unforeseen circumstances, one hundred years later there will probably even be a President Johnson in the White House!

A State Is Born

Every school child is exposed to the history of the beginning of the United States, and a thrilling story it is. Fighting for independence, drawing up a constitution, forming a government, struggling, growing; it is all in the textbooks. However, now, almost two hundred years later it is easy

104

to take all this for granted. Just reading about it puts it in the category of something that happened in the dim past. There are no eyewitnesses left to talk about those exciting days.

The thirteen original colonies had the painful struggle of breaking away from England, but once that was accomplished they all became states at once. No waiting around, no debates about whether they should be voted in; they *were* the United States of America.

New states were added, after first going through the territorial stage, asking to be admitted and then being voted upon by Congress. The wait was not unusually long; events moved rapidly in those days with the Westward expansion.

The Civil War decided whether the United States would remain united. Soon after, at the time when Alaska was bought, the states numbered thirty-seven. Other Western states were added until 1912 when Arizona, the last of the Lower-48 to be admitted, was voted in with hardly a ripple.

Juneau waterfront from docking Alaska State Ferry. Freight docks and fish processing plants line the waterfront

Contrast the admittance of the frontier state of Alaska with her frontier sister states to the south. As territories, they advanced to statehood within a reasonable length of time. But from the time Alaska became a territorial part of the United States till she was admitted as a state in 1959, the span was ninety-one years! Even Hawaii, admitted a year later in 1960, owes her lesser struggle to the fact that Alaska broke the ice.

That Alaska became a state in this very generation makes it easy for anyone interested to uncover the story. Just ask any Alaskan. A good opening question is "Why did it take so long?" People who have written books on the subject are still very much alive to defend their views. And anyone who read the newspapers or listened to the news in the 1950's could hardly have missed this controversial part of Alaska's story, almost too new to be called history.

Why Did It Take Ninety-One Years for Alaska to Become a State?

"To make a long story short—and it *is* a long story," a former territorial governor of Alaska comments, "looking back over those years one word sums up the whole situation—neglect."

This former governor is well qualified to speak on the subject of Alaska statehood. Ernest Gruening, governor from 1939 to 1953, was elected to the Senate when Alaska became a state. In Washington, D. C., Senator Gruening, Senator William Egan (later Governor of Alaska), and Representative Ralph Rivers persistently carried on the battle for statehood from 1956 till the bill making Alaska a state was finally ratified in 1959.

In his book *The State of Alaska* Senator Gruening thoroughly defines what he means by neglect. The first seventeen years of United States sovereignty he labels total neglect; the next fourteen, flagrant neglect. The next fourteen he describes as mild but unenlightened interest followed by twenty-one years of indifference and unconcern. Finally he concedes a growing awareness from 1933 to 1954, leading to the final statehood struggle and victory.

Looking back, it is always possible to analyze a situation and figure out why certain things may or may not have happened. That is where the old adage "hindsight is better than foresight" came from. In the case of Alaska, there were many foresighted people, but they were a frustrated group. Their hands were tied by red tape, and they were completely baffled by directives issued by uninformed men a few thousand miles away. Uninformed in this sense meant clinging to the various kinds of false information dispensed in the purchase debates. Later descriptions, even from people who had firsthand information of Alaska, did little to dispel these impressions. They were often advanced by representatives of wealthy, powerful interests who had their own axe to grind in Washington. In many cases this was how to take the most wealth out of Alaska with the least possible cost.

Though Alaska can be compared in some ways to other frontier territories that went through certain channels till they achieved their full place in the Union, the one great difference is in the timetable of progress. It took seventy-five years to gain the rights of American citizens as enjoyed by other territories under the jurisdiction of the United States. These rights do not seem phenomenal: mainly, having a state legislature, and representation in the United States Congress by Alaskans aware of Alaska's needs. But these rights were absolutely essential

Orthodox crosses on ornate houses for spirits indicate Russian influence at Indian cemetery near Anchorage

to start the process of developing the country and to achieve law and order and self-government.

For the period of total neglect, nothing was legislated in Washington to further these ends. Alaska was a forgotten land, and the only authority (not legally sanctioned, at that) was military. No one could *legally* stake a claim or be punished for a crime or even be buried or married! The rulers of Alaska in constant parade were the captains of various ships dispatched to Sitka harbor to try to keep law and order in the lawless, leaderless capital.

It was during this time that Alaska, unlike the other frontier states, had her only difficulties with native uprisings. Though the resentment and antagonism of Indians was a persistent threat and deterrent to pioneers of the Westward Movement, Alaska—except for this one era—has gotten along well with her native population.

Nowhere have excuses been made for the behavior of the Americans; the Indians were more badly treated than under the Russians, and the natives were justified in rebelling. The ensuing lawless and unmanageable situation was further complicated by a remunerative traffic in liquor, dispensed to whoever was willing to pay the price. Naturally those on the receiving end of the high profits wanted it to continue. Clear heads were hard to find in Sitka. The situation could not become much worse; it had to become better. But how could this be accomplished?

One of the very basic needs was the opportunity to acquire land so that taxes, essential for the support of government, could be levied against land-owners. From taxpayers are drawn juries and elected judges and other essential offices. Towns and counties, schools and churches can be established. Constantly improving means of transportation and communication can be provided. A voice in the central government at Washington with representation and protection for the resources of their territory then follows as night after day. In short, the desire of the people living in Alaska was for a gradual but progressive achievement of all rights and benefits of civilized living, as granted to all other citizens of the United States.

Alaska's plight was complicated, not only by the indifference of its far distant center of government, but also by the extremely inadequate means of transportation and communication serving such an isolated land. But Washington was not entirely deaf to the pleas, especially as the desperation and fear of Indian reprisals became more acute. A feeble attempt was made to improve matters by passing the first Organic Act, giving Alaska its first laws.

This act gave Alaska an appointed governor, a Federal district judge, and four lesser judges. Unfortunately, the rest of the provisions were hand-me-downs, based on the laws of the Territory of Oregon.

To be workable, laws governing any country, state, or territory have to be based on the characteristics and needs of the land. Even if the Oregon laws had been suitable for Alaska, those sections that would have given the Alaskans the territorial rights they were seeking were stricken from the act for Alaska: no revision of land laws for homesteading, no counties, no congressional delegate, and no Alaska legislature were to be permitted. Almost anything Alaskans had in mind for bettering their lot was interpreted, in the Oregon law, in terms of established counties and school districts. These did not exist in Alaska, nor could any be formed. The act was worthless; though it sounded as if the Washington administrators were willing to have local authorities go ahead, the tools were not provided for doing so.

Sending a governor to this outpost of the United States in 1885, however, was a step forward. He had the authority of his office and without doubt his instructions from Washington. The rub was carrying them out or, in fact, enforcing and cracking down on a host of elements that had by now gotten out of hand. The first governor, John Kinkead, was familiar with the problems of Alaska, having been one of the first to arrive in Sitka after the purchase. However, after his lone report, written after being governor only twenty-six days, in which he ably summed up the reasons why the situation was impossible, he headed back to Nevada when his brief term was over.

The second appointed governor, Alfred P. Swineford, deserves honorable mention for effort. He was an Outsider, but extremely capable and threw himself into his job with courage and energy. Blessed with vision and realizing the great potential of Alaska, he felt something should be done about it. He wrote four annual reports, each a literary masterpiece protesting conditions in the territory. He had the skill to do this, for his former job was editor of a Michigan newspaper, and he used his talents to the utmost.

Governor Swineford sounded off on all the important issues. He hammered away at the unworkable form of the civil government. He complained bitterly at the injustice being done to Alaskans through withholding political and other rights automatically granted to all other holdings of the United States: Puerto Rico, Hawaii, the Philippines. Labeling the civil government of Alaska a burlesque was one of his milder terms. He was deeply concerned over the health and welfare of the natives and the need for conserving natural resources of furs and fish. He worried about education and law enforcement. He pointed out in no uncertain terms that he felt powerful lobbyists in legislative meetings were throttling Alaska with no concern except their own selfish interests. He also called them liars, out-and-out misrepresenting the true picture and values of Alaska. And he pounded his fist, at least on his desk in Sitka, trying to emphasize the urgent need for life-saving representation for Alaska in Washington.

What really beat this dedicated man was the communication system, or rather the lack of it. In 1885, it took at least three months for a round-trip exchange of a letter and reply. And the reply, when it finally arrived was usually a refusal to recognize essential needs. That is the way it was for almost every basic issue for the first seventy-five years of United States ownership of Alaska! Other governors followed, repeating the same sad song like a broken record. Capable and vociferous in protest, dedicated in purpose—Governor Swinefords in government, as in any other field, are few and far between.

Complaints continued to be registered, though they seemed to be falling on deaf ears. Every change in administration was scrutinized hopefully. Every legislature had a number of bills dear to the hearts of Alaskans. The issues were growing and the wording was more explicit, but the theme was the same: full territorial status, delegate to Congress, homesteading and land legislation favorable to Alaska, and revision of laws so they could apply to Alaska. The word carpetbagging, borrowed from Civil War days, came into use again. Alaskans wanted appoint-

Fur seal harem in the Pribilof Islands. Depleted by early exploiters, herds are now protected by the government

ments, since they still were not allowed self-government, for all civil offices filled from the ranks of Alaskans, not Outsiders, referred to as carpetbaggers.

A bill the governors begged to have passed was for a ship for administration use. Not a luxury yacht; any old ship that would get them to the far-flung places they were ordered to inspect and report on a certain number of times a year. It seems ridiculous when you can hop a plane to almost any village in Alaska now, but in those days transportation was a real problem. Congress had not an inkling of the amount of time it took, for example, to inspect the seals in the Pribilof Islands about fifteen hundred miles from Sitka.

For the appointed judges to hold court in Wrangell for just one day it took a month of preparation, including getting there. And once there, juries were illegal because without landowners there were no taxpayers to serve. Small wonder the laws could not be enforced; jails just weren't big enough to hold that many people the length of time it took the judge to make the rounds.

The Post Office Department had never heard of the slogan "The mail must go through"; at least they had no intention of applying it to Alaska. Governor Swineford gave them the most trouble. They retaliated by being most uncooperative, even when captains of various ships in and

111

out of Sitka offered to carry the mail *free* as a favor to the isolated town. Mail hardly seems like a forbidden item, but it was bootlegged along with whiskey, only without profit.

In all fairness, the Federal government, over several administrations should be given credit for some accomplishments and concern for Alaska. A Native Service under the Department of Interior was established as early as 1884 for aiding and educating all native groups in Alaska.

Alaska's distinctive flag design was created in such a school by a thirteen-year-old orphaned child in 1926. Benny Benson was living at the Jesse Lee Mission Home in Seward. He entered a contest held in the Alaska Public Schools by the American Legion for designing a flag for Alaska. His simple design, eight gold stars on a field of deep blue—seven stars forming the Big Dipper and the eighth, the North Star—won.

Equally simple but effective was his concise explanation for his choice of design: "The blue field is for the Alaska sky and the forget-me-not, an Alaska flower. The North Star is for the future State of Alaska, the most northerly of the Union. The Dipper is for the Great Bear—symbolizing strength."

Indian and Eskimo girls contend for the title of Queen of Eskimo Olympics at Fairbanks

The Government even imported and supported reindeer-herding because of concern over the plight of Eskimos, whose economy and way of life were being changed by slaughter of caribou on which they had been dependent. Washington was also ripe for a second look at Alaska after what has been referred to as its third discovery—gold. The other two discoveries, of course, were by the Russians and Seward.

But there was not enough action for energetic do-it-yourself Alaskans. There were incidents like the Cordova Coal Party in 1911, protesting coal lands being closed to settlement and mining. Alaskans dumped a cargo of Canadian coal into the harbor of Cordova, in the tradition of American Revolutionists who dumped a shipload of British tea at the famous Boston Tea Party.

In 1906 a delegate to Washington, though he had no voting power, was granted to Alaska. Next the Organic Act of 1912 finally gave Alaskans the territorial right to have a legislature. This new act had many restrictions imposed by ever-active private interest lobbyists, but it paved the way for the meeting of the first Alaska legislature in 1913. With this first limited milestone in self-government, the legislature passed welfare laws and gave women the right to vote in Alaska years ahead of the rest of the nation.

All that the state's legislature was allowed to do was recommend on the many controversial rights requests. These same requests continued to be ignored for the next forty years. All those years, however, the recommendations of the Alaskan legislature were kept alive and before Congress by the untiring, but voteless, Alaska delegate.

Symbols for Alaska

Even in the early legislatures, time was devoted to discussing and choosing symbols for representing and furthering the spirit of Alaska. All on its own, Congress in 1884 had a seal designed and made for Alaska, presented with its limited provision for civil government and the first appointed governor. It was used until 1910; then Governor Walter Clark complained it stressed icebergs, natives, and northern lights too much. He wanted other sides of Alaska represented, too: fishing, mining, agriculture, furs, seals, and even the proposed railroad. The final design,

including the old as well as the new, was substituted when Alaska advanced from a District to a Territory in 1912. In Alaska's Constitution, provision was made that this same seal, a little over two inches in diameter, was to have the word Territory changed to State whenever that long-sought and happy event should occur.

The third legislature felt especially patriotic and concerned with symbolism, for it met just fifty years after coming under the United States flag. Besides the traditional American holidays, this legislature declared holidays on Alaska's milestone days. March 30 was called Seward's Day in honor of the Treaty of Purchase. October 18 was set aside as Alaska Day in tribute to the raising of Old Glory on the day of actual transfer from Russia to the United States. It also honored the prevalent and delicate forget-me-not territorial flower. Could there have been a political hint in this choice?

114

In recent years an official song was chosen; the King Salmon was named State Fish; the Sitka Spruce, State Tree; and the distinctive and changeable Willow Ptarmigan, Official Bird. And if a State Dog is ever selected, chances are it will be an Alaskan Husky.

Victory at Last

The first bill asking for statehood was presented on March 30, Seward's Day. The year was 1916! Of course, nothing happened. Alaska had reached an awkward age, a between-discoveries period which was to continue for twenty-five years. The rest of the United States during that time was very much involved in serious foreign and domestic problems: World War I, and then an economic depression. Each successive administration had its hands full; it could hardly see beyond its own office desk, let alone try to understand the problems and needs of a territory five thousand miles away.

Not that Alaska was ignored completely, by any means; this passage of time merely serves to answer our original question "Why did it take so long for Alaska to become a state?"

In fact, it took a fourth discovery of Alaska—this time by the Japanese after the bombing of Pearl Harbor—to focus attention on this potential state. In the next several years Alaska grew in importance when it was clear that the United States was vulnerable to invasion by the Japanese via Alaska. The enemy had already set foot on the most Westerly portion, the Aleutians.

By the end of World War II and during the years following, great changes and advances in transportation and communication were taking place. The population was changing, both in number and type of people. Certain areas had been thrown open to homesteading. People carving a permanent home out of wilderness were worthy and able to face up to the job of advancing the cause of statehood. The appeal of Alaska reached out to soldiers and airmen who had been stationed in various sections during the war and to construction workers who had been a part of the mighty projects necessary for defense. They returned to settle with their families. It was the same with government workers.

No longer an isolated, unknown land, Alaska was becoming a visitors' attraction. A new industry, tourism, was developing. People were interested in touring up the famous Alaska highway. They wanted to explore the trails where gold miners trod and see the colorful, historic towns. Many were attracted by reports of superb fishing and hunting.

But the wheels of the Federal government were still grinding too slowly to suit Alaskans. Now there were a great many more of them giving voice to their desires. Two of the most hackneyed objections to admitting Alaska as a state were deing dispelled. It no longer was important that Alaska was not physically touching the other states. Advanced means of transportation were shrinking distances there, as well as around the world. And they could now argue that the population, though still sparse compared with other states, was as large or larger than many a territory that went through the same transition from territory to state.

The beginning of the final battle was in 1955. In a drastic mood, the legislature appropriated $300,000 for a constitutional convention to be held at the University of Alaska. It took seventy-five days for fifty-five delegates to draw up a constitution to suit the needs of Alaska. It compared most favorably with any of the other state constitutions.

The eyes of all Alaska, if not the rest of the United States, were on this convention. No time was wasted in ratifying the constitution. At the next election in April, 1956, the vote was in favor, two to one.

Statehood bills had been regularly submitted to Congress by Alaskan delegates for many years, and with various rewordings and changes. Basically, they were requesting the very same rights that the first legislature had. The conclusion drawn was still the same: that Alaska could never realize its destiny and fully advance till it became a state. The efforts so far had been just as futile as in the past.

Now, armed with the new Alaska State Constitution, the three delegates—Gruening, Egan and Rivers—moved to Washington in 1956, ready to do battle. They were prepared to stick with the issues until they could write "mission accomplished."

No doubt the debates were just as opinionated, even as bitter, as the debates in 1867 over whether to buy Alaska in the first place. And they went on much longer. It was three years more before Alaska became the forty-ninth state.

Realistic Alaskans do not look on statehood as a sort of genie which will solve all problems automatically. Statehood is not an end in itself, but a means to an end. Wise planners for Alaska realize the important decisions to be made: what, today, are the true resources and values of Alaska and how can they best be administered and preserved?

As in all democracies, there is not complete harmony and agreement. However, most citizens of Alaska understand and agree that the selfish, fleeting, bonanza dreams of years past will not work for a progressive future. Goals must be set and the many tasks at hand attacked with all the vigor these modern-day pioneers can command. They have known, themselves, for almost a century that they are equal to the job; now is the chance to prove it.

January 3, 1959, the day Alaska officially became a state, joins the ranks of other Alaska holidays. January 3, 1967, eighth anniversary of statehood and Alaska's Centennial Year, marks the start of a year-long birthday party. A year is the *least* time Alaskans feel it should take them to celebrate all that they have to celebrate!

Travel—by Dog Team or Jet

Alaskans, past as well as present, have always been a mobile people. Migrating to the continent in the first place involved considerable traveling. After they got there, it was necessary for survival or for bettering their status to be able to move freely about their vast land. The reasons for migrations have remained about the same; the primary difference is in methods of accomplishing them.

Travel by land and sea has been well used for centuries. Walking and carrying on his back everything needed for a primitive household were perfectly acceptable till man devised easier and better means—perhaps a man-powered sled, forerunner to one pulled by a team of dogs. And so on to the modern automobiles, trucks, trailers, and campers you see on Alaska's ever-growing network of highways.

The sea surrounding Alaska on three sides was a constant challenge. It was a source of food, as were the many rivers pouring into it. Sea creatures were needed for clothing; boats and other items were absolutely necessary to native welfare. The sea was also a barrier when, in lean times, it was necessary to search for greener pastures on nearby islands and distant mainland. Thus, it was not surprising that early Alaskans became excellent boat makers and adept seamen. Their lives depended on it: Alaskan waters are chilly; even expert swimmers can survive only a few minutes in an upset, due either to inferior workmanship or lack of skill. Today native kayaks are seen still plying Alaskan waters, along with large and small private boats of all description and a modern, state ferry-system.

Keystone Canyon, scene of historic railroad battles. Unfinished roadbed now is Richardson Highway

119

Eskimo family leaves Point Barrow for month long caribou hunt in walrus skin oomiak powered by big outboard motor

To the above means of travel a new dimension has been added in just the last half century: travel by air. Alaska claims a substantial contribution to the world's progress in the use of airplanes for transportation.

"Alaska was the cradle of the development of commercial aviation," states Jim Dodson, veteran Alaskan pilot who has flown all types of aircraft from early days to the present. "First came the experimental stage in the twenties, followed by the pioneering stage—and now jets."

Alaskans, whether they live in metropolitan areas or small, isolated communities, at one time or another find themselves making use of all these methods of transportation, from dog team to jet plane. Moving people and the materials that they need to establish homes, build careers, and develop resources is a constant and fascinating job. Transportation—all kinds of it—is the lifeline of this frontier state.

A Half Century of Air Travel

The scene is Anchorage International Airport. We enter the large, modern terminal building that could be the pride of a city five times as large in any other part of the world. Outside, the sound of an intercon-

120

tinental jet plane approaching or leaving cuts through the normal busy hum, and in the twilight lights blink on the control towers. A pleasantly pitched voice, traceable to an attractive, neatly uniformed Eskimo girl in the information booth, announces arrivals and departures and other pertinent information over the loud speaker.

Approaching the information desk is an East Indian woman, dressed in gold-threaded crimson sari; on her feet are the traditional sandals. We hope the girl at the information desk, as she answers the visitor's question, will also warn her that she will need warmer clothing if she plans to venture out in the chill of Anchorage's early spring weather. But the chances are that the lady is only passing through via a polar route on her way to warmer climates.

"Good to see you back, sir," an aide salutes his colonel, and they walk toward the baggage department together. The officer has been away on military business and is now returning to his base at nearby Elmendorf.

A stewardess comes through the gate with a small Eskimo in tow. Whether a boy or girl it would be hard to determine under the layers of parka with not a hair showing to give a clue. Obviously, the child is ill; the typically stoical little face is flushed, and the eyes are bright with unshed tears and fever. He—or she—trudges along with the kindly stewardess, no doubt headed for treatment at the Alaska Native Service Hospital in Anchorage.

Two Seattle-recruited construction workers with battered satchels shake hands as they part company, one to continue on to Nome, the other to remain in Anchorage to work on a new apartment building.

"Let's keep in touch," says the Anchorage man. "Fill me in on what it's like up there. Maybe I'll join you for that long, light summer I've heard about."

"More likely *I'll* be ready for the big city by then," laughed the other man. "Unless I manage to strike gold and stake a claim!"

From scraps of conversation, appearance, and other hints the occupations and destinations of the hurrying throng become evident to the interested eye. There is an oil man from a rig near Kenai, whose company has given him a round-trip ticket to California for his periodic two-weeks leave; a group of electronics experts headed for a DEW Line (Defense Early Warning) outpost; school teachers, government workers, and native fishermen or cannery workers transferring from bush planes that pick them up in small villages to jets that will take them to Bristol Bay. Thus the main airports at Anchorage, Fairbanks, and Juneau are earning their place as crossroads of the world in air travel.

An interesting phenomenon occurs in jet air travel between Anchorage and Seattle, due to the difference of two time zones and the fact that the state of Washington is on Daylight Saving Time in summer. Leaving Seattle on an evening flight, a traveler arrives at Anchorage five minutes before he left Seattle, according to the airport clock. By actual time, of course, it takes just under three hours to travel the 1450 miles. By Jet Clipper, you can now arrive at Fairbanks seemingly ten minutes after leaving Seattle. A special treat is a three-hour sunset that grows brighter as the plane approaches the northern destination.

"Apparently I never will become a sophisticated traveler," remarks Byron Fish, world traveler and *Seattle Times* columnist. "Little things like that still strike me as gee-whiz marvels."

Smaller than Jets

Jet planes are only a small part of the air picture in Alaska. Almost every hamlet has its airstrip, but few have population enough to handle the larger plane traffic. Thus many other types of aircraft are absolutely essential to keep goods and people moving all over Alaska. They vary in size, ranging all the way down to private puddle jumpers, which line a small lake near the heart of Anchorage, wing tip to wing tip, like huge flies ready for flight. A recent tally indicates there are 549 airports in Alaska.

Plane shapes are varied, too. Funniest, perhaps, are the awkward-looking Grumman Goose and Widgeon, named for the birds they resemble. Not the most modern planes now, these amphibians are still the best for some places in Alaska because they can land on either land or water, whichever is available. People flying in big jets to Ketchikan on Revillagigedo Island in Southeast Alaska have to land first on nearby Annette Island, the only level spot large enough for an airstrip. From the island,

122

Hundreds of float planes line twin lakes, Hood and Spenard, near Anchorage International Airport

passengers are ferried by amphibians to the Ketchikan waterfront. These planes, at home on either land or water, use their wheels to leave Annette airstrip but land on their hulls in the harbor. These assorted aircraft are used for typically Alaskan purposes. Per capita, there are more private planes in Anchorage than anywhere else in the world. Alaskans fly more air miles than travelers in other states.

"Having a plane in the family in Alaska is like owning a boat in states where the fishing is good and water is accessible by car and boat-trailer," Jim Dodson points out. "It is not unusual for a business man to get up early in the morning, fly to a favorite fishing spot, and get back to his office desk in time to put in a full day's work. The long hours of daylight in summer make this possible. If he doesn't have his own plane, there are many bush pilots who are in business to see that he gets his wish."

Besides recreational uses, planes are often the only regular contact and source of supply for many isolated communities. Many small airlines owe their existence to what they call milk runs. Though larger cities may be served by other means, many little towns depend on daily air service for supplies, passenger service, mail, and even laundry.

Another use of planes has grown with the tourist industry in Alaska. Flightseeing, from a quick trip over the impressive Juneau Ice Field or over the icebergs of the Glacier Bay area to an overnight stay at an Arctic Coast town above the Arctic Circle, is possible only by plane. More daring pilots supply food and equipment drops for parties scaling the massive Alaskan peaks, whether the motive is recreation or scientific research.

The government Fish and Wildlife Service has its own planes kept busy with game surveys, fisheries management, law enforcement, and research. Spotting and counting large herds of caribou and keeping track of moose and all types of bear, from polar to grizzly, can be done most advantageously by air. Their planes have carried many strange cargoes.

"I'll never forget my first summer with the Fish and Wildlife Service," recalls a game surveyor. "Our chore that year was trapping, tranquilizing, and then transplanting wild mountain goats to various mountain foothills!"

Bush Pilots

Much has been written about Alaskan bush pilots, real pioneers in aviation. They were intrepid men—and sometimes women—who had the vision to know that some day airplanes would be an essential link between Alaska and the Outside.

As late as 1924, the dog team was Alaska's main means of transportation. But that summer, Noel Wien, a barnstorming circus-flier, accepted an offer to fly in Alaska and made the first flight between Anchorage and Fairbanks. From then on, Fairbanks residents became accustomed to the sight and sound of Noel Wien's plane as it headed toward mining camps and villages on commercial flights to the Interior. That first summer was especially notable for lack of prepared landing strips. However, he survived, and this was the beginning of forty successful years of flying and the founding of one of the main regional airlines, Wien Air Alaska. This airline has grown and kept pace with the times; the order is already in to add jets to its fleet.

Noel Wien was soon joined by many other pilots intrigued with aviation possibilities in Alaska. These pioneer bush pilots are especially revered by old-timers who lived in the Alaskan bush. They may not recall the governors, mayors, presidents, or other important people of the 1920's, but without hesitation they can name the bush pilot who brought them their mail or helped them out of a tough spot.

Classic stories of bush-piloting come from the Aleutians, where flying visibility more often than not is near zero. A flight-tower attendant at Adak airfield tells this story on Bob Reeve, now president of Reeve Aleutian Airways. Bob had a reputation for daring, and was especially noted for flying dynamite to miners in the bush. During a typically dense Aleutian fog, the tower received an urgent, radioed request from Bob to turn on all the field's available landing lights. The tower answered that it would do no good, the fog was so thick and, "Your request for permission to land is refused."

Came Bob's answer: "I'm already on the ground; all I need is light to find the hangar!"

It appears there will always be a place for the bush pilot and small plane as long as there are mountain climbers, prospectors, movie companies, hunters, fishermen, oil companies, and just plain sightseers. And airplanes usually have the right-of-way, though one pilot recalls having to watch out for buffalo on the landing strip at Big Delta. A traffic sign along a main road instructing cars to stop for planes, however, looks perfectly natural in Alaska.

Travel by Sea

Whistles blow, bells clang, and the sprightly sound of a pep band drifts over the narrowing expanse of water as a large blue and gold ship approaches the dock of a Southeast Alaska town. Shouted greetings are exchanged as passengers crowd the decks. Fluttering from high spars are the Stars and Stripes and the Alaska State Flag: the seven gold stars of the Big Dipper and the North Star on a field of blue.

A vantage point on the top deck gives a good view of a tug-sized boat approaching. Suddenly a siren cuts through the happy cacophany, and huge jets of water dart from the boat in several directions.

"There's the fireboat," someone shouts.

The fireboat salute is Ketchikan's contribution to the full-scale welcome. The long, narrow shape of the city makes a fireboat the most practical means of protecting the business district, which stretches along the waterfront within squirting distance of an unlimited hydrant of saltwater. Behind Front and Mission Streets, which form the main drag along the waterfront, the residential section hangs steeply with a wooded mountainside for a backdrop.

The townspeople have reason to be in a festive mood. This is the inaugural voyage of the *Malaspina,* flagship of Alaska's new State Ferry System, formally opening the long-awaited Marine Highway in 1963.

Streamlined ferry boats built to carry one hundred cars and five hundred passengers ply the Inside Passage

The route is old; the Inside Passage has long been used for sea travel. Traders, explorers, and natives used it in early days; freighters, cruise ships, and small private boats traverse it in modern times. The newness lies in the concept that this route should be considered a unique but regular part of the State Highway System.

When isolated cities need to be connected with each other and inland points, engineers start thinking of overland highways and the most practical, least expensive way of doing the job. In this case, they were stymied by Southeast Alaska's mountain barrier. The initial cost of a conventional highway would be staggering, and so would the annual maintenance per mile. Building a ferry fleet to provide regular service on this natural and well-used water highway seemed to be the best answer.

Once the decision was made, the job was tackled in high style; the state had three miniature, but luxurious, ocean liners built, each with a capacity of five hundred passengers and one hundred cars. They were christened *Malaspina, Matanuska,* and *Taku,* named for three large glaciers.

The run starts in Canadian territory at Prince Rupert, British Columbia; Ketchikan is the first Alaska port of call. The ferries then continue on up the Inside Passage, stopping at the main cities to deliver passengers and freight.

The Marine Highway has been expanding. The *Tustumena* and the *Chilkat* connect Kodiak Island, the Kenai Peninsula, and Gulf of Alaska cities. Canada's *Queen of Prince Rupert* is the newest link south to Vancouver Island. Local ferries carry on from there to Puget Sound country.

The Interstate Commerce Commission periodically wonders whether this marine route should properly be called a highway. Alaskans have no doubts and figure they have gotten their money's worth already. Along with delighted tourists, they consider riding the ferries more relaxing and more fun than driving.

The atmosphere aboard is most informal and friendly. There may be a lively Indian dance going on in the lounge: just the costumed Chilkat Dancers from Port Chilkoot on the way to perform somewhere and getting in some extra practice. An entire student body may hop a ferry in support of their team playing the high school at the next town up the waterway. Businessmen often prefer the more leisurely pace of the ferry to that of a plane hop. They can relax and get some work done on the way to an appointment. Frequently there will be a gay party in evening dress, on its way to a formal function at a neighboring Elks' Club or Arctic Brotherhood.

This is one highway that traverses hundreds of miles of scenery that looks the same as it did a hundred years ago; it might even stay that way for another hundred—or more. And it is still full of surprises. The Alaska Travel Division is telling the truth when it advertises: "Around the bend: a school of whales, a field of wild flowers, an unclimbed mountain, or maybe an old Russian trading post!"

Land Travel

There are many varieties of sea and air travel available, and they are widely used. However, land travel always has been (and probably always will be) the most popular method used by the greatest number of people.

"Jet travelers, cruise-ship passengers, motorists, and even motor cyclists and bicyclists we are used to seeing," Mike Miller of the Alaska Travel Division remarked. "But even we were amazed to hear of a hiker who walked literally all the way to Alaska!" A Seattle schoolteacher, Parker Sielar, had trudged more than twenty miles a day for ninety days, arriving in Fairbanks in late August one year.

Many trail routes are the basis for modern roads now connecting the important cities and trade centers of Alaska. Airways were ahead of highways as late as 1941, when there were less than four hundred miles of roads but thousands of miles of air routes. Railroads came before either, and were often hot on the heels of adventurers toiling over mountain passes. Before railroads, travel was by dog team. Dog teams are still a symbol of Alaska and indispensable beyond highways, railroads, and landing fields.

"In the early days of mail-plane flying, I can remember following a dogsled trail below me to keep from getting lost," admits veteran pilot Jim Dodson of Anchorage. In 1964 the last short mail route by dog team was finally replaced by plane.

128

Alaskans, especially those who own a working team, take their huskies and dogsleds as a matter of course. To them, they are just part of the scenery. Visitors, however, are usually much intrigued, and having heard of the part dogs have filled in Alaskan history, their first question is "Where can you see them?"

Summer is not the time to see them at work. In the Arctic, Eskimos call summer the season of poor sledding. In villages and Indian summer fishing camps dogs sit morosely chained to individual posts, just out of reach of the next dog. On racks nearby and also out of reach is the ever-present and odoriferous drying fish, the dogs' staple food. When they are not working, these dogs are fed a minimum ration, which does not improve their dispositions. The story in the villages is that some dogs are smart enough to sit on their chains to make them appear shorter, in the hope of snatching a bite from an unsuspecting and unwary visitor!

Sympathetic dog-lovers might question the practice of chaining dogs. For one thing, the dog population is too large to let them run loose to

A dog team is chained short most all summer at Kotzebue. Most dogs are chained in back yards because the beach is the main street

fight among themselves and get into the hanging meat and fish. Some trainers claim the boredom of being confined to a four-foot radius makes the dogs all the more enthusiastic for work.

As with most animals, their disposition depends on their treatment: how they are handled and how much they are fed. In winter, it takes two or three pounds of fish per day to feed adequately a sixty- to eighty-pound sled dog. As pups, they wander freely around town and are the most lovable little balls of fur imaginable. It is hard to resist picking them up and cuddling them when you stumble over them, and the native children give them lots of petting. Kindly masters value their dogs very highly, and recognize the need for exercise even in summer. They use carts on wheels for this purpose. Some, realizing the tourist potential, even have a little business advertising, "Sled-Dog Rides Here"; both dogs and visitors seem to enjoy the fun. At McKinley National Park Headquarters rangers schedule dog-sledding demonstrations, mounting wheels under a typical sled, and they answer questions about the dogs asked by interested bystanders.

More than one family touring Alaska has brought back a small husky pup as a souvenir, sparing the dog a life of toil and acquiring a faithful, gentle pet. One case in particular was a half-husky, half-elkhound puppy named Alyeska, who was born in the very shadow of Mount McKinley and lived at wilderness Camp Denali till her family discovered her. She lived in their tent with them and camped all the way down the length of the Alaska Highway to their home near Seattle, Washington.

The veterinary doctor warned the family about the reputation of this type of dog and prescribed firm but gentle handling, as he gave her the puppy shots. Though supposed to be an outdoor dog, she moved into the house and appeared as much at home as the three youngsters in the family, the first to answer the blast of the dinner whistle and quickly identifying everyone by name. But her ancestry shows every time the family takes off for the mountains. Alyeska sniffs the snow, tosses it high with delight, and burrows a snow nest, wrapping her curly tail around her nose for warmth. She ecstatically pulls with every muscle when hitched to a sled, all the while giving short joyful yelps.

Husky Dog Teams

Among Alaskan dog owners there have been many discussions about what constitutes the true husky strain, and what breed makes the best work-dog. The Siberian Husky is the only breed recognized by the American Kennel Club. Interspersed with the facts are tales of personal experiences. A storyteller might concede he would not be there except for his sturdy dog team and its especially intelligent leader.

The typical sled dog may be quite a mixture, including wolf, and dating from dogs the Eskimos brought with them from Asia. These were probably a hardy polar dog like the chow or elk hound. The husky is considered by many dog enthusiasts to have been contaminated during gold-rush days by the infusion of many mongrel types from the waterfront of Seattle and other jumping-off places for Alaska. It is common knowledge that unscrupulous ship captains used to shanghai a crew when shorthanded. Apparently dogs, much in demand for packing by the frantic miners, were also stolen and shipped north, where their mortality rate, unless they were especially strong, was especially high. At any rate, there is evidence of many other breeds of dogs among the Alaska work-dogs of today, wherever they are found.

Huskies are medium-longhaired dogs, and in winter grow a soft underfur for extra warmth. Unofficial weather predictors claim the thickness of this undercoat is a clue to how cold the winter will be. Huskies have a rather seedy look for a while when they shed the no-longer-needed underfur in large, woolly tufts. Their tails are bushy and their legs are strong; their mighty lungs are housed in broad, deep chests. They have tremendous endurance and ability to withstand below-zero temperatures. Even their feet are geared to arctic living and are so tough and protected by hair that they are not easily cut by ice and hard snow.

"Huskies are most beautiful dogs, some with a typical and distinctive mask," remarks Josephine Crumrine, noted Alaskan artist. She prefers to paint dogs, and has done many choice portraits, fully capturing their alert, intelligent expression.

It is likely to be a long time before anyone invents a better or cheaper

method of moving supplies in ice and snowbound communities in isolated parts of Alaska. Although planes can land on skis, there is still the problem of getting goods from the plane to the families in the towns. The sight of dog teams and sleds lined up to receive freight from a small jet airplane is most symbolic of Alaska at the present time. Even the most modern developments occasionally run headlong into frontier barriers, and the age-old methods take over.

There are a few signs of mechanical snow-vehicles replacing dogs. "Some natives have found it cheaper to buy gasoline than to fish all summer, dry the fish, and then feed it to the dogs in winter," commented an Alaskan.

Not only the dogs have to be rugged. It takes stamina for a man to jog along at a good clip behind a dogsled for many miles a day following a trapline. The sledder has to be resourceful and able to deal with any emergencies, for he is often all alone and miles from possible help. There

132

has to be a mutual respect between him and his dogs. There are times when he has to rely entirely on the uncanny instincts of his lead dog to avert catastrophe. Dogs know when it is too cold to survive and indicate it is time to hole up till better weather. When the temperature drops below – 50°, a wilderness jaunt becomes a survival test.

Dogs have to respect thoroughly their master's authority. When he gives the command to "Mush!" (slurred version of the French word *marchons,* pronounced *marshon* and meaning "Let's go") every dog on the team has to do just that.

When weather reaches many degrees below zero at night, the musher very likely depends on his dogs for warmth to keep from freezing to death. The dogs are used to burrowing and curling up in the snow and their bodies give out a lot of heat. Thus the expression "it was a two-dog night or a three-dog night" means the sledder, by cuddling up to that number of dogs, was quite comfortable.

There are many tales where individuals have been saved; one memorable news story in 1925 told how a whole town was saved through the use of dog teams. Nome, on the edge of the Bering Sea, was still ice-bound and isolated in the early spring. A small child became ill with a sore throat.

Nome's doctor was uneasy from the time he examined the child's throat and suspected that the cause of the high fever and pain might be highly contagious diphtheria. Moreover, he learned that the child had been playing with many others in town. It appeared that a diphtheria epidemic which could wipe out most of the town's population was in the making. The nearest life-saving serum in adequate quantities was almost seven hundred miles away.

A plane and pilot were ready and waiting in Fairbanks to attempt a mercy flight but flying was very new, and the odds were too great against his getting through. The weather was extremely bad and there were no instruments to help in those days. If he crashed, all the available serum would be lost with him.

The harbor was filled with ice, and even under summer conditions a boat would be too slow. The only possible chance of getting the serum to Nome was by dogsled. Judged by the time it normally took for regular mail runs, this would not be fast enough in the dire emergency. To sled anything in to Nome from the starting point of Nenana, a distance of 674 miles, took a month in winter. When one after another, three Nome children died of diphtheria, the mayor, doctor, and city council met to see if there wasn't some way of getting the serum in time.

In Alaska there is an unwritten code that anyone in distress must be helped. The serum was gotten to Nenana, and from there on it was in the hands of the very best teams and sledders available along the mail route. At every stop a fresh team was waiting; no run was shorter than twenty-four miles and the longest was ninety-one miles! The best speed achieved was a little over ten miles per hour. The phenomenal race with time was won in one hundred twenty-seven and one-half hours—less than six days.

The Alaska Highway

For four generations, farsighted individuals had been dreaming of a land route to Alaska. However, it took a major catastrophe to start the bulldozers rolling. Almost simultaneously with the bombing of Pearl Harbor, the Japanese landed troops on the farthest-out islands in the Aleutian chain, Attu and Kiska. Fear of further Japanese invasion and possible cutting off of water lanes to Alaska led to the rapid construction of the Alaska Highway, surely one of the greatest engineering feats of modern times.

Most of the 1522.8 miles of highway from Dawson Creek, Canada, to Fairbanks, Alaska, had to be whittled out of an almost hopeless wilderness of dense forest, streams that could flood without warning, and massive mountains.

Speed was the keynote of the construction of the Alaska Highway. The quick decision by the United States, made within two months after Pearl Harbor, started the building; the construction was completed only nine months and six days later. Probably never before was so much high-powered machinery concentrated on one road job, nor such a price paid—one hundred thirty-eight million dollars.

In May, 1942, U. S. Army engineers unloaded their bulldozers from train cars at the end of the railroad line at Dawson Creek in the center of

British Columbia, Canada. These troops of the Army engineers fought hard. The enemies on their front were mosquitoes, mountains, mud, and muskeg. They did the dirty work of pushing the pilot road through, then passed it on to others to finish: the U. S. Public Roads Administration contractors and the U. S. Engineers Department.

A fabulous amount of heavy machinery speeded completion of the highway, but much of the credit must go to the tremendous manpower employed. Eleven thousand troops built the pilot road; up to sixteen thousand civilian workmen improved it. Over eight thousand drainage culverts were installed. Bridges laid end to end would have a total length of more than seven miles.

"The heartbreaking part of bridge building," an eyewitness declared, "is that so many of the bridges had to be built over again when a mild-looking stream went on a rampage."

The rapidly moving history of the Alaska Highway had its high points. One was the meeting of the two pilot-road construction crews; the one working north from Dawson Creek, and the other working south from

Alaska Highway, built in World War II, winds 1400 dusty miles through Canada. Alaska portion is blacktopped

Whitehorse, Yukon Territory. On September 23, 1942, they met at Mile 588, appropriately named Contact Creek. Another highlight was the official opening ceremony at Soldier's Summit, Mile 1061, on November 20, 1942.

The Alaska Highway *might* have met the fate of many another military road built under great stress, and reverted to the jungle. Instead it has been steadily growing and improving in the last quarter of a century.

However, it is still far from a freeway. There are long stretches with few signs of civilization and slight traffic. This encourages an occasional bear or moose, sometimes with a young one, to wander right by the road. A sight like this is enough to make you realize you are indeed traveling a genuine wilderness road.

With its easy access to the South-48 states and all the color and lure of Alaska like a pot of gold at its end, it would be hard to find a road in this day and age better suited to satisfy a traveling family's craving for adventure. The best time for travel along the highway, though, is open to debate.

"Winter, after the first snows become hardpacked," say Alaskans, accustomed to dealing with such conditions.

They feel three main drawbacks are thus eliminated: dust, washboard surface, and insects. However, extremely low temperatures are hardly suitable for family camping expeditions. The best time for vacation travel is July to September. Before July, travel is likely to be bogged down because of spring thaws in some places.

The highway is not one interesting sight after another, and it is long. Barren, monotonous sections seem to roll on for miles at times before eyes have the relief of a beautiful mountain or varied blue lake. It's a lonesome road, too.

"I'll never forget the lonely, helpless feeling I had watching my truck burn up, the tires exploding one after the other," says one traveler. "No water, only a small, inadequate fire extinguisher—not even a shovel. After what seemed ages I was joined by a couple of other cars, but all they could offer was sympathy and a ride to the nearest place where I could get organized again, about twenty-five miles away."

Maintenance and administration of the Alaska Highway may always present problems because of the physical features of the land it traverses. The Canadian portion, about four fifths of its length and much of it still unpaved, was turned over to the Canadian government after the war.

The Alaska Road Commission handles the Alaska portion, which is all blacktopped but in a perpetual state of construction and improvement. However, today's road crews, in comparison with those who first worked on the pioneer road, have more chance to admire the spectacular scenery: snowy peaks, blue lakes, pristine forests, and beautiful rivers.

The highway ends in Fairbanks. A hint of highway conditions found by early summer travelers was in this whimsical announcement heard over the local radio station: "Test drive your Ford on Fairbanks streets!"

The Richardson Highway

The Richardson Highway, oldest road in Alaska, is a road hewn by history. Its gradual, and sometimes painful, evolution is also the story of the evolution and improvement of land transportation.

The route was first a trail used in 1899. Before that, the avid gold seekers had to wend their way over the difficult and dangerous Valdez Glacier trail. Next it was used by dog teams, followed by pack horses. An amazing amount of freight was moved that way in early gold-rush days. Some of the first ores from nearby rich mines were taken to market over this sled route, but the cost of freighting was so high it was hardly worth the mining company's trouble.

By 1910 the road was widened enough to be called the first highway to the Interior and Fairbanks, and was named for Wilds P. Richardson, first president of the Alaska Road Commission. He had done much of the early mapping and exploring, following a military mission under Captain W. R. Abercrombie.

Now the Richardson Highway is a fine, blacktopped road, but through all its evolution there was surprisingly little change in the route followed. The southern end meets cold Alaskan waters at Valdez, once a a noted supply port and point-of-entry for gold seekers. The northern end joins the Alaska Highway and is defeated by permafrost and tundra above Fairbanks.

The one hundred twenty miles in between contain a cross-section of Alaska's beautiful and spectacular scenery: a sampling of glacier, tundra, high mountain, and river valley. One scenic highlight is Thompson Pass, where a panorama of snowclad mountain peaks unfolds. In narrow and beautiful Keystone Canyon, traces of an old road can be seen precariously clinging to the cliffs above.

"The pleasure seeker will find much enjoyment in a buggy ride along the road constructed by the Alaska Road Commission to Keystone Canyon, fourteen miles distant, where the Bridal Veil and other beautiful waterfalls may be seen," wrote John Underwood, newspaperman and author early in this century.

"The horse-and-buggy set in those days had a most thrilling ride," confirms his widow, Helen, in recalling an early trip up the canyon.

In this same canyon, easily seen by the side of the road, there is an old handcut railroad tunnel, never completed. Though more than one railway company attempted to establish a route, this tunnel gives mute testimony of their failure. Rex Beach, famous writer of Alaska adventure stories, immortalized the colorful, often violent, events of those days in his novel *The Iron Trail.*

The whole area around Valdez is steeped in gold-rush history. The town's citizens through an active, historically minded Chamber of Commerce have carefully mapped out the area and put up signs so visitors

Unfinished railroad tunnel near Valdez, scene of an historic construction battle

Alaska Railroad freight train winds along the shore of Kenai Lake. Passenger trains are streamlined

can find some of the mementoes. There is a Chinese burial ground, for many of the mine workers came as cheap labor from the Orient. And what frontier town would be complete without a Hanging Tree? The beginning of the Valdez Glacier Trail morbidly reminds visitors that those crevasses still hold countless men and horses and tons of equipment, lost in the mad gold-scramble.

Even though paved and much traveled now, the Richardson Highway, with thick forest and glaciers coming down almost to its very edge, has never lost the feeling of a pioneer road.

Railroads

Railway promoting in Alaska followed the gold strikes, but not only gold was being discovered in many parts of the territory. Prospectors recognized other minerals of value—huge copper deposits as well as coal in certain areas. The wealth was there, but the payoff depended on getting it from mine to market. Hopes were high, and people with money to invest were especially interested in the transportation problems.

It is hard to visualize just how difficult it was for those hoping to prospect and mine to keep life-sustaining supplies coming *in,* besides solving the problems of getting the product *out*. If a person runs out of something today, it is a short trip to the supermarket or machine shop. In those days, it meant a wait of many months or doing without it entirely. Sometimes it became a matter of life or death.

Railroads appeared to be the best answer. The successful building of the White Pass and Yukon Railroad over the Trail of '98 from Skagway to the Yukon in 1900, only two years after the first prospectors started toiling over that killing route, was most encouraging. It led to schemes promoting short railroads to take ore out of the wilderness to a more convenient shipping point. Actual construction began on some, but many others did not get beyond the worthless paper-stock stage. Others were used only as long as a mine was producing and then were abandoned.

It was hoped, of course, that railroads would do for Alaska what railroads had done for opening up frontiers of the rest of the United States during the Westward Movement. The theory was correct, but the odds of accomplishing this in Alaska were against it. There were no bulldozers in those days! Solid rock had to be attacked with pick and shovel and dynamite. Rail beds had to be smoothed by horse- or man-drawn scrapers. Manpower was always a problem. Every new gold strike left Alaska construction crews shorthanded. On one memorable work day on the White Pass Railroad in 1899, fifteen hundred employees grabbed their picks and shovels—and took them along to stampede at Atlin, British Columbia. Since Skagway was a thousand miles from supplies, the picks and shovels were as hard to replace as the men.

No doubt because of the success of early railroads in the United States the government was convinced of the potential value of railroads in transportation and supply in Alaska. At any rate, Congress passed a law in 1914 authorizing the President to "locate, construct, and operate" railroads in Alaska.

Though Congress gave the green light to the Alaska Railroad, it was not completed for many years. World War I depleted manpower for construction work, and other problems prevented its full opening until 1923. The occasion was important enough for President Harding to go along on the first ride; it was the first time a U.S. President had set foot in Alaska, though it had been a rich possession for over fifty years. Much of

140

the time, however, the Alaska Railroad appears to be still under construction. Road crews are constantly repairing damage caused by the extreme cold.

"These rails were heaved up when the roadbed froze and the earth expanded," points out the road-crew boss. "When it warms up this spring, it will thaw and sink."

In winter you wonder how they do it, but the train makes a complete run twice a week—up one day and back the next. In summer this most northern railroad in the Western Hemisphere makes a daily run each way, taking on freight at Seward and passengers from Anchorage to Fairbanks, a total distance of 470 miles.

Weather is not the only winter hazard on the railroad, There is a footnote on the Alaska Railroad's timetable that states: "Not responsible for delays because of moose on tracks."

This is not just Alaskan humor. It is a fact. Moose apparently are convinced that this path cut through deep snow and maintained by snowplows is especially for them. They pay no attention to moose turn-offs cut into banks; they are so heavy (twelve to fifteen hundred pounds) that they walk right through fences. They wouldn't think of getting out of the way when pursued by the mechanical monster. They just trot ahead of the train, where the walking is easy. If at any point they happen to get the feeling that they are cornered or become just plain annoyed, they will turn and fight the monster.

Most of the time the train wins. In front, what is ordinarily called the cowcatcher is facetiously referred to as the *moose-gooser*. An electric-shock, prodding attachment has met with only moderate success. As many as three hundred moose a year are killed by collision with the train. It is impossible to make that many emergency stops, especially when rounding a corner. Thus the Alaska Railroad helps furnish a good portion of the meat for the native hospitals and orphanages of Alaska.

Even the kind of railroad bridges is dictated by the moose. Ties have to be solid so they can get across. It would mean a long delay to try to extract a moose, dead or alive, whose long legs had slipped between bridge ties, leaving it belly-down and helpless on the track.

Eskimos above the Arctic Circle

What is so unusual about a tree growing in the Arctic tundra? The amazing thing is that it clings to life in a treeless environment. It is a fact that trees do not grow in tundra, especially above the Arctic Circle. Most of the year the terrain is white and frozen. For a short season in the summer the arctic tundra comes to life with low vegetation, swampy lakes, and even flowers. But no trees.

Then how does this tree happen to be growing near the government building on the outskirts of Kotzebue, thirty miles north of the Arctic Circle? Perhaps someone planted it as an experiment—or a joke. A sign by it says "Kotzebue National Forest." Many people have looked at this tree; sophisticated tourists laugh at the sign as they think of the lush stands of timber they have seen or of the trees that grow with little effort in their yards at home. Small Eskimo children who have never seen a tree before are more impressed.

"I couldn't take my eyes off the trees the first time I went Outside," said one young Eskimo. "They still fascinate me. When I came home I brought all the pictures of trees I could carry."

This lone tree, whether it dies or somehow manages to survive and adapt to its new environment, could be considered a symbol of native groups at the present time—the descendants of the original Alaskans. It is of hardy stock and its roots are firmly in place. Now it requires a certain amount of care and nurture from those who cherish it.

So it is with Eskimos in the far north. A new, though perhaps not better, culture has been introduced, placing the Eskimo in a position

Fourteen-year-old Eskimo girl carries her brother in the back of her roomy parka

where he has to change and adapt. Part of his basic economy, acquiring food, still depends on his age-old skills. Through association and dependence on outside influences, he has now acquired a taste for additional needs that can be supplied only by money. He has to be able to compete for, and hold down, a job. To help him help himself to realize his potential, a certain amount of care and nurture by those who introduce the new ways is essential.

Today there are many individual cases that can be cited where natives have weathered the changes to become an integral part of modern Alaska. This, of course, is the ultimate goal. Being aware of the problems and working toward a solution is the task at hand. How successful the outcome will not be known for many years.

Eskimo Towns

Anyone who writes about Eskimo towns today runs the risk of having his observations out-of-date before they are printed. These towns *are* changing rapidly, and there are many who believe that eventually the changeover to white man's ways will be complete. The Eskimo with all the cultural and racial qualities the name now implies will no longer exist.

Meanwhile a visit, even fleeting, to an Eskimo town gives a most fascinating opportunity to observe the old and the new at work and play. Perhaps right now is the final chance to experience fully this interplay of ancient and modern forces; in a very few years the pendulum will no longer swing into the past.

Drastic changes are likely to bring pangs, especially to those most affected. However, it would be hard to find a people who are taking them with more grace. Moreover, they remain a happy, cheerful people with an excellent sense of humor, adapting readily as the need arises. Those who study people and their racial characteristics say this philosophical outlook is due to their environment. Centuries of adjusting to, and accepting, a cold harsh world have disciplined them to adapt to almost *anything.* They had to be intelligent and ingenious people to survive. These same traits make them most valuable citizens of the state of Alaska.

"Many old people like me like talk about old days," confided eighty-year-old Bert Johnson, who was still a spry dancer. "Never want to go back—*much* too hard." Then he added with a twinkle in his eye, "Eskimo same as white man. *He* no want to go back to bow and arrow —'cept for fun?"

On a map, the larger towns like Point Barrow and Kotzebue can be pinpointed, as well as some of the smaller ones. They have interesting-sounding names like Shishmaref, Noatak, Selawick, Gambell, and Point Hope. These towns, many of them above the Arctic Circle, and some smaller villages make up a large, but sparsely populated Election District. Ninety-one percent of the population is native Eskimo, and so is their elected legislator. As foremost citizen, Senator Eben Hopson from Point Barrow gave the opening speech first in Eskimo, then in English, at the first Eskimo Olympics held in Fairbanks.

Kotzebue, home of the tree, is a good place to start in our tour of Eskimo towns. It is an old town, dating from about 1500. For centuries, Kotzebue has been the center of trade and transportation for the Arctic. Eskimos have been used to infiltration by Outsiders: Siberians, Russians, Norwegians, and now fellow Americans. They were discovered by a Russian naval officer in the early 1800's. He wandered into the Sound while looking for a Northeast Passage and found a thriving Eskimo town on the somewhat sheltered shore. Its Eskimo name, *Kikitagamute,* quite musical-sounding when pronounced by an Eskimo, was changed to the less tongue-twisting Kotzebue in honor of the captain.

Kotzebue today is still a busy and growing town. The mostly native population reflects its many outside influences over the years. Yet many of the age-old ways are evident to visitors walking along the main street. This street is actually the beach, and the scene of much activity during the short summer season.

Like most arctic towns, Kotzebue can be reached only by air. For the benefit of tourists, the plane pilot makes sure all his passengers are aware they are crossing the Arctic Circle. He flashes the "Fasten seat belts" sign, and then at the proper point salutes the spot with a big lurch of the plane. You then know you are at latitude twenty-three degrees and twenty-seven minutes distant from the North Pole. Later each passenger is presented with an Arctic Circle Certificate signed by the whole crew.

Sometimes the pilot will spot a giant herd of reindeer grazing in the arctic tundra and will circle it to give passengers a closer look.

Approaching Kotzebue, the inexperienced person finds it hard to spot the airfield in the vast, monotonous expanse of tundra. The flat, boggy, brushy terrain, punctuated with infinite small lakes left by the melting snow, seems to go on forever.

This first bird's-eye view of Kotzebue is not impressive, and this is true of the other Arctic towns. A row of weatherbeaten, mostly unpainted, small frame buildings faces the water. Other slightly more impressive buildings are the stores and hotels. In contrast are the white painted government and military buildings. A short distance away is the inevitable and starkly marked cemetery.

Homes in the Arctic

"Where are the igloos?" someone is bound to ask. It is hard to overcome preconceived notions of Eskimoland, even if you visit in midsummer, when the snow and ice are gone for a short while.

Though legend has the Eskimo living in an igloo, this is probably the one thing you will never see. Alaskan Eskimos do not use igloos as permanent dwellings. However they still do build them when they travel in winter by dogsled over the snow-covered tundra. When it is time to camp, natives will watch for an area of the right kind of snow: hard-packed by wind to a foot or so in depth. Then, cutting hard snow to handy-sized blocks, they stack them, like bricks, curving inward to form a dome-shaped structure. A couple can build a family-sized igloo in one or two hours. Try it sometime; it will take a novice all day.

The Eskimo homes at Kotzebue are typical, though maybe a little better than elsewhere. They are made mostly of logs, but supplemented with driftwood, sod, and boards. Since there are no trees in the area, the wood has been brought in from some distance, perhaps from Southeastern Alaska on the once-a-year boat, or floated down from sparse forests up the Noatak River about forty miles away. Considering the effort expended to acquire these houses at all, a visitor used to more attractive dwellings should think twice before criticizing their drab appearance.

The typical house is a single story, built in a long, narrow shape with a

June ice breakup on Kotzebue Sound, north of the Arctic Circle. Graveyard for Eskimo village of Kotzebue is at lower left

dugout, gravel-floor cellar underneath. All of them are built with long vestibules, enclosed storm porches for protection from wind and snow. These storm porches serve as storage for frozen reindeer meat and essential paraphernalia. Sleeping rooms are on one side and an oil-stove-heated kitchen-living room on the other. Few Eskimo homes have sinks and running water, but almost all have electricity.

"An electric refrigerator looks like a normal piece of equipment," said a social worker who has visited several homes, "but it is surprising sometimes to see a Stereo Hi-Fi set dominating a corner of the room!"

Keeping the exteriors painted for the sake of beauty would be a waste of time and money, considering Kotzebue's short summer. Nature does her own inimitable job with pure white snow and ice the rest of the year. As one becomes accustomed to the appearance of the town in general, it all seems appropriate for the country. The seedy appearance of buildings points up all the more the contrast of bubbling good spirits, gay parkas, and energetic activities of the townspeople.

At more remote and primitive villages most Eskimos live the year round in sod huts, called *innis*. These are made of tundra blocks, chunks chopped from muskeg, constructed and shaped just like ice igloos. There is one sod hut at Kotzebue, but no one lives in it.

The sites around Eskimo dwellings, especially in the out-of-the-way old villages are considered gold mines to archaeologists who excavate them. In kitchen middens have been found all sorts of fascinating implements and household articles, making it possible to reconstruct ways of life in different eras. A midden is merely the garbage disposal of the Eskimo housewife. Through the ages she tossed outside everything she didn't want inside; it was consumed by dogs, if edible, or covered over by winter snow and summer vegetation, layer upon layer. Frozen and refrozen, the refuse builds up, waiting for an inquisitive scientist to start digging.

The oldest artifacts found at the bottom of some heaps in Alaska were believed to be two thousand years old. However, a recent Brown University expedition made discoveries that set the date back another two thousand years.

The diggings are near the Kobuk River, about fifty miles north of the Arctic Circle and one hundred miles from the Bering Strait, along the route that it is believed man first traveled to this continent. The expedition from Brown University found the remains of what may be the oldest house in North America. It was described as round with central heating —a fireplace in the middle of the sunken dirt floor. Since only the floor was left, the scientists could only guess at the wall construction—probably igloo-shaped, with the willow frame held together with sinew or leather from the animals they were hunting then.

Everyday Living in Kotzebue

Some part of everyday living in Kotzebue has to be given to taking care of items that are taken for granted in most other states. Primitive living conditions are always time-consuming. The water problem is one example, though it seems odd in a land noted for ice and snow. The trouble is that water is not in a usable form till certain things are done to it.

The long Kotzebue peninsula is too flat for fresh water streams, and nearby lakes are frozen two thirds of the year. The nearest source of water is a lake two or three miles from town. In winter, ice blocks are delivered by dog team for ten dollars a ton. They are stacked and stored along the outer wall of houses to be brought in and melted as needed in fifty-gallon drums, just inside the central section of the house. Some homes have a shallow well and hand pump in the basement, but the water is very hard and only good for washing.

In summer, from June to November, water is delivered by water truck and barge for four cents a gallon. It comes from the Noatak River many miles away or from a small creek below town. This water is carefully tested and chemically purified before it is declared safe for drinking by those who worry about such things.

Natives are not quite so particular. In June, when the ice breaks up in Kotzebue Sound, big chunks of fresh-water ice flow past their doorsteps from large Selawik Lake, thirty miles away. For about a week, perhaps more, they have a handy, if not completely sanitary, water supply. Children and adults are out chipping away at the ice at all hours, filling up big drums next to their houses. The rest of the time they have to haul their water from the nearby lake by dogsled, or buy it, if they can afford it.

Because of the frozen ground, plumbing—as we know it—exists only in the modern hotel facilities where tourists stay. Probably visitors hardly realize what effort has gone into providing them with certain home com-

Eskimo housewife collects fresh-water ice from a nearby lake as it floats by on saltwater tide of Kotzebue Sound

149

forts. Eventually a solution will be found, but now all waste has to be carted away by truck at considerable expense to both residence and business.

If pure, palatable water and disposal of waste seem difficult and costly, think of the problems related to transportation and supply. There are no connecting roads to other parts of Alaska, and not likely to be any for a long time. Airlines bring freight as well as passengers, and there is one commercial freighter yearly which brings supplies for Kotzebue and surrounding villages in mid-July. A Government supply ship comes in August, and two oil tankers during the summer. There are no docks, because the Sound is not deep enough for boats to come closer than about twelve miles. All freight and oil have to be lightered from anchorage to town by assorted barges.

These things take money; besides providing a large part of their living through hunting and fishing as in the past, natives now have to work part of the time at jobs provided by a superimposed culture or depend on welfare.

"Year-round employment is limited," remarks a Friends' Service representative. "There are jobs for natives at the hospital and in the schools. There are also construction jobs as well as some types of work in private industry."

She feels that help is needed to suggest and create opportunities for work during this transition period. It is especially important to stimulate projects that give natives a feeling of responsibility and a chance to use their initiative in raising their standard of living.

"I was especially delighted with one new addition since I last visited here," she laughed. "Kotzebue now has a laundromat and dry-cleaning establishment. I wandered in and found half a dozen Eskimo women, some with babies tucked into their parka hoods in the traditional style, sitting and chatting away while their clothes were being washed."

A laundromat is a real boon, with the water situation as it is. There is now discussion of ways and means to build a community bathhouse. This could have far-reaching effects on the constant battle to improve public health.

In summer, when schools are dismissed, children of all sizes form an unofficial reception committee. Occasionally a visitor is startled to note a pair of bright blue eyes peering out of a round, rosy Eskimo face. Kotzebue's history helps to explain this. In the 1890's when whalers, manned by Scandinavians, were hunting in northern waters, some of the sailors settled in Kotzebue. There are also evidences of English, Japanese, Russian, and even Balinese mixtures; in fact, it would probably be hard to point to a truly pure-blooded Eskimo in cosmopolitan Kotzebue.

Children's clothing is varied. Some wear beautifully made little fur coats; others wear colorful cotton parkas with the fur on the inside. Bright, intricately machine-stitched rickrack designs decorate the outside. With this fancy, but warm, outer garment they wear a comfortable pair of mukluks, almost knee-high boots made of sealskin. The mukluks are invariably trimmed with borders of small pieces of skin or fur sewn in an attractive design. Sometimes the otherwise perfect picture of native dress is spoiled when you glance down at the feet. Instead of mukluks the child may be sporting proudly a pair of store-bought rubber boots. The Eskimo mother, no doubt with some begging on the part of a small son or daughter, has succumbed to the quicker, easier method of providing footgear—perhaps through a mail-order catalogue!

Actually, native sealskin parkas and sealskin mukluks are very practical for northern winters, and many white residents will be seen wearing them. Tourists are issued parkas by the tour hostess to wear while they are in Kotzebue. Though fifty degrees in summer feels like a heat wave to the Eskimos, visitors are grateful for the borrowed parkas with the fur-trimmed hoods to protect them from the brisk breeze often whipping waves along the beach.

You are probably wondering if it is possible to communicate with Eskimos as you stop to watch their activities or want to chat with some of the children who are your constant escort. Practically everyone speaks English, the children very well because they use it in school. Their parents speak both English and Eskimo, and the grandparents have picked up some English, but are more at home in the native language.

Eskimos are inclined to be shy, though friendly; they are not chatty. However, they seem willing to answer questions, even though tourists sometimes ask some pretty peculiar ones. The Eskimo mind is used to coping with practical problems which have to be solved quickly—for survival, in many instances. They are direct in getting to the heart of a matter and are very literal-minded. This sometimes leads to amusing conversations.

"How old is the baby?" someone will ask an older child carrying a little brother Eskimo-style in the back of her parka.

"He isn't *old* yet, only eight months," the child will answer, seriously.

If you ask who owns a certain little roly-poly husky pup frisking around under foot, someone will look around and then point out the mother dog.

Visitors are usually surprised when they ask the names of Eskimos to find Taylors, Nortons, Allens, Jones, and Johnsons well represented. Some common given names are Patricia, Ira, John, Victoria, Janet, Helen, Ida, Eddie, Bert, and Mary. They may also have Eskimo names, like Aknik, Seeganna, Tocktoo, and Kobuk, but most of them now go by the English, Scandinavian, or Russian names acquired by descent. Occasionally someone may take the name of an admired famous person. Outsider Terry Spring's first-grade teacher had trouble convincing him that Abraham Lincoln was *not* an Eskimo living at Kotzebue. The ride in Abe Lincoln's *oomiak,* a large skin boat, was to him a never-to-be-forgotten thrill.

Life is simple in Kotzebue; but providing just the essentials of food clothing, and shelter for a family takes a great deal of time and effort. A small part of the income may come from short-term seasonal jobs with a salary, but for most of the native population the greater part of their economy depends on age-old skills. Hunting and fishing are serious business. During summer they must catch and preserve a winter food supply for their big families and a team of ravenous dogs. Everyone pitches in, even the children, to help garner an adequate supply of seal and whale meat and fish.

In food, as in other essentials, you find the old and the new. Parents and grandparents still have a yen for real Eskimo food, like blubber, seal oil, strips of dried fish, and other edibles foreign to white culture. But they also use canned and powdered milk, canned goods, and other items which can be bought in the store. If you peek into an Eskimo's handy permafrost deep freeze, you will probably find some T-V dinners stashed with the frozen caribou and reindeer.

Eskimo children, living in a cosmopolitan town like Kotzebue, have succumbed to the charms of Outside food, especially candy. Unfortunately visitors are susceptible to the longing looks in small Eskimo faces, and this generation's teeth are showing the effects. It could be the amount of candy consumed! It appears that today's children are less enthusiastic about the old types of food.

Even in more remote villages there is evidence of changing food habits. A school project in one small town was a study of nutrition, which led to gathering Eskimo recipes. The youngsters compiled a book from the information gathered from elders on edibles in the Arctic and how to prepare them. The directions were written in the children's own words. Quite often the child's outspoken opinion of the dish was included. Along with the recipe for Soured Seal Liver, made by covering the raw liver with blubber and letting it stand a few days till ripe, was this frank comment: "Most of the boys and girls don't like it, except the grownups and old people. I don't like it either."

Summer Activities

Fortunately, the summer days are long—twenty-four hours long. In fact, at Kotzebue the sun doesn't set at all for thirty-six days; eighteen nights before and after the longest day of the year. And, of course, it does not rise for that many days in midwinter. During the summer nights it swings eastward low in the north, describing an arc a little way above some peaks of distant mountains. Pre-sunset colors in the sky sometimes last for hours.

In the daytime the sun completes its circle by swinging to the east, south, and then west. With all that daylight, there is always activity along the beach. Visitors have a tendency to lose track of time. Trying to keep up with the perpetual and fascinating activity is exhausting. Natives simply go on working till they get tired and then go to bed till they feel like getting up. Their meal times are just as informal. Youngsters often fish off a seaplane pontoon or just play long after midnight.

To keep tourist-native relations on a tactful, friendly, informative basis, a hostess usually goes along with a group of people seeing the

By light of the midnight sun, boys fish from pontoons of plane beached at Kotzebue

Multiple exposures of the sun, shot every twenty minutes on the longest day of the year. Lowest image, fourth from left, was taken at midnight

town. She tells them a little about the natives, introduces them by name, and encourages questions and answers about their activities.

Strolling down Main Street, the beach, after the ice leaves the Sound in late May or early June, you are likely to see the men out sprucing up their boats, ready to go hunting seal and whale. There is quite an assortment, most of them now powered by a motor.

The women tend their gill nets almost in front of their doorsteps, paddling about in little rowboats and skiffs. They spend long hours cleaning and fileting their catch and then hang it on endless log racks to dry in the sun and wind. As seal and whale are brought in, they butcher them deftly using their short, curved woman's knife—called an *ooloo*— and prepare the winter's food supply. They dry sealskins, scrape them, sew up the openings, and blow them up to form pokes to hold whale oil. In big iron pots on the beach they cook *muktuk,* an ominous-looking black delicacy made from whale skin.

At sight or rumor of the small white whale, or *beluga,* there is much excitement. Men take off in their motor launches in hot pursuit. The twenty-foot whale are generally shot with a rifle, then harpooned, and tied to the side of a boat for hauling to shore. Beluga are most common from breakup of ice in early June to mid-July, though their appearance is spasmodic all summer. Meanwhile, the shore is lined with eager onlookers, and the youngsters rush forward to beg a small piece of flipper, one of the old foods they still love. The hunters indulgently cut off and distribute the treat, which the children immediately pop into their mouths—raw.

Seal are caught in much the same way, though the best sealing is done before the ice breaks up. Much more prevalent than beluga, they may even be shot and retrieved from the village beach. April and May are especially interesting months for hunting and fishing. Eskimos then are still fishing through four or more feet of ice with carved ivory minnows and non-freezing, fibrous, whalebone fish-lines for shee fish, or jigging for tom cod. As farther distant, more-open ice starts to break up, natives load tents and kayaks on dogsleds and mush great distances to open water to hunt seal. The hunting is strictly man's work; women butcher the kill, do most of the fishing, preserve the food, and sew the clothes.

Eskimo mother mends her fish net in front of her home. Women do the fishing; men hunt

Hanging cleaned fish to dry at an Eskimo summer camp

Work and Play

Like their parents, the kids of Kotzebue lead a busy life. Their activities depend on the season. In winter they attend school. In summer they are expected to help with the chief family project—gathering and preparing the winter food supply. There are always chores to do.

Eskimo children appear to develop a sense of responsibility early in life. Older children look after the younger ones. In the back of their parkas, older sisters carry babies too small to walk, a sash tied around their waists and under the baby's bottom. A slightly older child will gently lead a toddler back from the water or a chained husky dog.

"Puppies won't hurt you," he will explain, "but big dog might bite if you get too close."

Of course it isn't all work and no play. Children's games are much like those of children the same age everywhere. Boys play cops and robbers, but the characters are probably hunters and polar bears. Little girls play with dolls, dressing and undressing them in beautiful little fur and cotton parkas. They skip rope, swing on the school swings, and teeter-totter Eskimo style. Instead of sitting, the two players jump on the ends of the plank and bounce the other one as high as they are able.

Though it is during the long dark winter that people have the leisure to relax and play and feast on their summer labors, they are always glad for an excuse to take time out for fun. Almost every night there is a native dance in the armory. This is encouraged by the tourist promotion element in Kotzebue, but from the enthusiasm of the performers, it would be hard to say who gets the most out of it, dancers or spellbound audience.

Children join in dancing and singing, learning the traditional folksongs and motions of the dances from an early age. You see them in the background following the motions of their parents. Occasionally a few little ones are encouraged to step out and perform. Some are as young as three years and the oldest dancers are in their eighties and still light on their feet. They are delighted if, during specified dances, their guests will join them.

Dancers wear their most colorful parkas and mukluks. The other essential part of the costume is a pair of mittens. The ancient significance of the mittens seems to have been lost, but as a solo dancer gets up to perform he puts them on before beginning.

The accompaniment is provided by a chorus and orchestra consisting of round, flat skin-drums about thirty inches in diameter. These are moistened with water many times during the evening to keep the skins taut and in good tone. Dancers and musicians sit on benches at one end of the building; spectators line the other three walls.

The dance rules for men and women, who perform separately, are somewhat different. Men are allowed more freedom of movement and can lift a foot off the floor while using vigorous hand motions. Women are supposed to keep both mukluks on the floor, often staying in one spot as they perform their graceful arm and body motions in unison. When the dance calls for traveling, they use a sliding, shuffling step. From the actions it is easy to see that the dancers are acting out a little story in pantomime. The master of ceremonies translates the chant-like song, which is sung in Eskimo.

Eskimos are noted for being great storytellers; telling tales was one way they whiled away the long winter evenings. Their songs reflect this; many tell of age-old happenings and have been handed down word for word, note for note over the centuries. They also have their contemporary songwriters, like the popular songwriters of today, and their creations tell of current events. The favorites are repeated, and some will no doubt be handed down to future generations.

Some of these Eskimo popular songs really break up the natives in the audience. From the sly glances directed toward the tourists and many giggles, one might guess that the translation given may be slightly altered. But even these new songs are in the Eskimo scale with a typical rhythmic beat. There is no recognizable rock 'n' roll or take-offs on American songs. Though with their sense of humor and willingness to adapt, some singer—tongue-in-cheek—might sometime come up with an Eskimo version of "Who Put the Overalls in Mrs. Murphy's Chowder?" It will no doubt start out "Who Put the Mukluks in Mrs. Kobuk's Muktuk."

Eskimo visitors from towns farther away sometimes summer in Kotzebue. The Diomede Islanders, noted for their skill in ivory-carving, have been coming regularly for as far back as anyone can remember. It is quite a boat trip across two hundred miles of open sea, even though the big walrus skin *oomiaks* are now powered by thirty-five-horsepower outboards. For probably half the distance they are fairly near to shore. The Islanders' work is artistic and often made of fossil ivory found in the area or of walrus tusks.

Many Eskimos work full or part time for the airlines, the main boosters of the fast-growing tourist industry. Jobs vary: some work for the hotels; some highly-trained, skilled natives pilot planes or help maintain them. There are public relations jobs like supervising *oomiak* and sled rides, which the friendly residents fill with apparent enjoyment. Guiding the operation will be a parkaed, smiling Eskimo, whose dogs are obviously eager and happy for the unexpected exercise.

Kotzebue is the State Police headquarters of Northern Alaska, and there are also a city police force and jail, quite new.

"The ladies were so proud of this new building, even if it was a jail, that they celebrated its opening with an afternoon tea," a member of the Kotzebue Chamber of Commerce recalled. "Right in the jail, of course."

The United States Government also has a White Alice installation for long-distance communication and weather reporting. Much of the weather for the Pacific Northwest is forecast from information on what's going on in the Arctic, relayed from Kotzebue.

Guests are encouraged to join Eskimo dancers at Kotzebue. Girl in white parka is an airline hostess

Point Barrow

Many of the same situations and conditions described at Kotzebue will be found at other Eskimo villages in the Arctic. The more remote, less accessible villages are bound to appear less sophisticated because of less contact with the outside world. For example, after a visit to Point Barrow, farthest-out Eskimo settlement of the United States, Kotzebue with its few advances toward modern comforts appears almost luxurious.

"It is interesting that twenty years have passed since war forced Barrow's close exposure to outside influences," noted a resident. "Yet Eskimo is still the main language, and the natives still depend on a hunting-fishing subsistence."

Barrow, like the other villages, originally had an Eskimo name that simply meant the point. This point jutting out into the Arctic Ocean is readily seen on maps as you follow around the northern coastline. A British explorer discovered the town over a· hundred years ago and named it for an English polar explorer, Sir John Barrow. The town is far from all the others, and there are only a few nomadic Eskimos to the west and east. These are gradually moving to Barrow to settle, where there are schools, health services, jobs, and other advantages.

King Island Eskimo ties thread harness on a delicate walrus ivory carving for which his people are noted

Over the years the natives had little contact with the outside world other than through adventurers, scientists, and archaeologists who wandered there. Until air travel developed, there were not too many of them. An air crash in the vicinity finally focused the eyes of the world on Point Barrow.

In 1935, Will Rogers, famous American comedian and his ace pilot, Wiley Post, headed to Alaska's far north for an adventure trip. Their plane went down near Barrow. An Eskimo and dogsled were the first to reach the wreckage and relay the sad news to the outside world.

World War II was the start of the transition of Point Barrow. Then the DEW line (Distant Early Warning system) was established there. Native manpower was needed along with the military, and many Eskimos adapted amazingly well to the new jobs. They were trained in communications, construction, clerical, and mechanical jobs. In return the natives were of the utmost value in helping the less-hardy newcomers learn the art and necessity of survival in their extreme and sudden change of environment.

The economy of Barrow continues to be dependent on government activity. It is the headquarters for the Arctic Research Laboratory, and several ice islands that are floating research stations are supplied and serviced from Barrow. This provides employment for some natives.

But there are now signs of an upsurge in the prosperity of Barrow, based not on the government, but on the efforts of the natives themselves. There are cooperative ventures underway for long-due town improvements. Of course, it will take time to accomplish urban renewal almost at the top of the world. But if town planners have their way, eventually Barrow will become a most modern Eskimo community.

First order of business was putting the town in order. The streets were narrow and zigzagged without reason, and the houses were placed helter-skelter. Town growth was according to whim, with no allowances made for community buildings. The population was estimated at about seventeen hundred Eskimos, three hundred non-Eskimos, and one thousand sled dogs. All wandered freely, without any legal right to the land other than squatter's rights.

"And don't think those one thousand—or more—sled dogs aren't an important part of the population," points out one of the town planners. "They are the real working members of the community."

That many dogs can also pose problems. Plans included facilities for dog tie-downs more sanitary and pleasing to the eyes and noses of the increasing number of tourists as well as of townspeople.

It is hard for a people used to a simple survival type of living to understand the upheaval necessary to give them a legal title to their property. These Eskimos have always lived at Barrow or in the vicinity. They like it there where the hunting and fishing are good. What difference does it make who owns the property? No one ever used to worry about who owned even a personal item. If someone needed to borrow something, it was unnecessary to ask. If the item was lost or broken while on loan, it was sufficient for the borrower to say he was sorry. It is this attitude which has frustrated non-Eskimos in charge of tools and equipment for various schools and projects. The Eskimo does not understand how anyone can attach any value to a mere object.

In the matter of owning property, State Senator Eben Hopson, an Eskimo who lives in Barrow, has tried to educate the natives. He explained carefully the benefits of getting title to their town land when Congress freed it from the Naval Reserve. If they owned their land and paid taxes on it, there would never be any doubt about their being able to live in Barrow as long as they wanted and to hunt and fish in the old ways. If they should decide to leave, the land had value and could be sold.

Improving the town, it was pointed out, would make life easier and better. Having been exposed to some of the comforts of a higher standard of living, the natives could understand this. The question was how?

To straighten and widen the streets, a number of homes had to be relocated. Areas in convenient places were set aside for civic uses. The job of improvement was accomplished by the first all-Eskimo contracting company formed. They invested in the necessary heavy equipment available at the nearby construction camp. They moved about ninety houses, built some new ones where necessary, and also built a new post office building, which they then leased to the government.

The next step was to provide cooperatively owned utilities. Natural gas for heating and cooking had been available to all government installations for more than fifteen years. It came from wells sunk in a vast natural petroleum reserve discovered nearby. But though the mains went right past the Eskimo village, the natives could not take advantage of the naval reserve's cheaper, handier fuel-supply for their own use.

Special legislation had to be signed by the President first. Then arrangements for financing, building, and operating the system had to be worked out. The Eskimos formed a utilities cooperative and borrowed money from the Bureau of Indian Affairs. Management of the cooperative, however, rests with the board of directors, all of them Barrow Eskimos.

Barrow already had electricity, but it was expensive for the same reason that heating was. The generator had to be run by oil, brought in by fifty-five-gallon drums at high cost. The utilities cooperative plans to buy the generating plant next and, by switching from oil to gas, cut lighting costs as drastically as they have cut the cost of heating and cooking.

Steps such as these go a long way to relieve the two miseries of the far North, cold and darkness. With the successful example set by other communities with similar problems, Barrow residents hope to conquer the permafrost eventually. Then perhaps they will achieve that other wistful dream of the Arctic: up-to-date plumbing and a free-running, pure water system.

Indian Arts

"The entire native population of Alaska was seventy-five thousand strong before the white man's invasion. But by the beginning of this century it had dwindled to a mere third of that number," said Carl Heinmiller of Port Chilkoot. "Indian tribes—Athapascan, Tlingit, Haida and Tsimshian—were cut in half. The Aleuts were even more unlucky; they were mowed down to a mere one sixteenth of their former size!"

Carl is the Director of Alaska Indian Arts, Inc., a program now sponsored by the Government under the recent Manpower Development and Training Act. His interest in natives stems from his World War II experiences, when he was a major and in charge of training aborigines for jungle warfare in the South Pacific Theater. Now he is still interested in native survival in Alaska and fascinated by their primitive art forms.

If the Indians appeared to be vanishing at the beginning of the century, that is not the case today. A large part of the rapid decline was due to disease brought in by traders, explorers, and exploiters. Measles wiped out whole villages. Today their numbers are increasing, because of the efforts of government and individuals and an effective public health program.

But the Indians, like all natives caught between two cultures, need help to become a contributing force to the economy of Alaska. Many have yet to learn the value of money and be shown how to solve their problems themselves. Because there is a lack of native leadership at the present time, this help has to come from the white man. To help truly and effectively, the white man has to respect the differences between

Teen-age Chilkat dancer and her uncle who is an instructor in the Manpower Development Training program at Port Chilkoot. He wears a genuine Chilkat blanket

native culture and his own. He has to help the natives work toward *their* chosen goals, not superimposed ones.

Such a man is Carl Heinmiller. Long before any government support was available, he and others were working on the problems in their community. The community actually consists of three small towns in Southeast Alaska: Haines and Port Chilkoot, lying side by side at the northern terminal of the Alaska State Ferry System, where a road connects with the rest of Alaska; and Klukwan, an Indian village twenty-two miles to the northwest. However, the students who are eligible for the training program (mostly Indian in this part of Alaska) come from many outlying native towns: Yakutat, Hoonah, Kake, even from Nunivak and Little Diomede Island (Eskimo), and Aleuts from Bristol Bay.

There is an interesting contrast in the ages of the three towns in this area. Haines (described in Chapter Six) started as a mission in 1881 and expanded during the gold rush. Port Chilkoot became a town after World War II. No one knows how old Klukwan is; even its name translated means "always the town."

Haines looks as expected; conventional, a frontier-type town, with signs of modern development and growth evident in new buildings and street paving. Klukwan looks the part of an Indian village, with unpainted frame houses, dugout canoes on the shore, and totems. Port Chilkoot, however, is not at all the conventional picture of a small town. It looks exactly like an old-fashioned army post, which is just what it started out to be. The plan of Port Chilkoot, though routine for the army, is unusual for a town. Large white buildings—formerly officers' quarters, hospital, guard-house and barracks—surround a large, central parade-ground. It was the first permanent United States Army fort built in Alaska, in 1904.

Port Chilkoot's metamorphosis from army fort to incorporated town makes a rather fantastic, but typical, Alaskan story. After World War II the post was declared surplus and put up for sale. Four families of young World War II veterans bought it—lock, stock and barrel. Collectively, these young people forming the corporation had seen the world; this beautiful spot at the head of Lynn Canal sounded like Utopia to them. They bought it "site-unseen." Their dream was to develop a tourist cen-

Chilkat Dancers in front of their tribal house at old army post, Port Chilkoot. Costumes were made by Alaska Indian Arts program

ter with emphasis on native arts and crafts. Most of the original founders are still in the vicinity; two are active in the Alaskan Indian Arts and Manpower Development and Training program.

Native Arts and Skills

Today, some twenty years later, Port Chilkoot is particularly noted for its artistic achievements. On the parade ground there is always something going on, from Indian dancers in their authentically reconstructed tribal house to carvers working in the open air on tall totem poles. Former barracks house workshops; and young Indians, adults if interested, and

167

even non-natives are being taught their cultural heritage: all sorts of native crafts and historic tribal dances and songs.

"Compared to other natives, the Alaska coastal Indians were wealthy," Carl Heinmiller was saying. "Seafood was abundant, so there was not the struggle for food. They lived a fairly comfortable life with leisure time for artistic things. And all this beautiful wood to be carved. . ."

He ran his hand over a log of Alaska yellow cedar on which two young men were carving in front of the tribal house.

"This totem will be delivered personally to the Mayor of Copenhagen when we visit there next summer," he continued.

"Yes, this design is authentic; all the ones we use are," Carl replied to

Replica of Indian house at Totem Bight State Park near Ketchikan. These elaborate houses were primarily for ceremonies

a visitor's question. "Come in the workshop, and I'll show you some dance costumes and props."

He led the way, and from chests and tables quickly assembled a display of masks, rattles, blankets, headgear, furs, and skins that looked as if they belonged in a museum.

"We made all these items to use in our dances—except the Chilkat dance blankets," he said, holding up a heavy shawl-like piece woven in bold white, yellow, blue, and black design. "Though we can duplicate the design in block prints on cloth, these genuine woven articles are very scarce. Only two old weavers are left, one in Klukwan and the other in Haines, who know how to weave these; and they may die before they decide to pass on their knowledge."

Getting native people to teach their old arts, especially to a white man was not easy. They had plenty of reason for being suspicious and Carl first had to prove to them his genuine interest and gain their confidence. He knew they were still holding tribal celebrations in which the traditional songs and dances were performed. Inside the stark, unpainted houses he knew there were examples of fine carvings of tribal crests.

"I learned as much as I could through museums, but was determined to get through to the source. I had to gain the confidence of the people of Klukwan who might help me learn, in order to perpetuate what, I felt, was a magnificent artistic culture."

How to get around the reserves and suspicions that had been accumulating for years was an obstacle that might have discouraged a less-determined person than Carl. He set about to prove his good will by helping the natives in any way he could. If you look for it, there is always plenty of opportunity to give help in any primitive area, and Carl gave his time freely as needed, from doctoring to representing them in court.

Carl soon realized why the arts and skills were being lost; the older members of the tribe were no longer anxious to pass their knowledge down to youngsters who did not seem to care about their heirtage.

"The place to start was with the young people—but how?" mused Carl. "One point both the elders and I agreed on was that today's young people need a guiding hand to help them develop worthwhile interests and keep them out of mischief! "

Chilkat Dancers call on tribal elders in clan house at Klukwan for help with old chants and dances

An Eagle Scout himself, Carl's solution was to organize a Boy Scout Troop which was predominantly Indian. The activities were based on developing Indian skills which might otherwise be lost. After starting his troop carving and dancing, Carl asked tribal leaders if they would help to be sure the work was authentic. When the older Indians saw their young people enthusiastic about learning the old dances and songs of the tribe, and saw them working on button blankets, carving dance masks and making costumes, they came through with much expert advice and guidance. By this time, Carl was so well thought of that he was adopted into the tribe and given a high and worthy Indian name in the Raven Clan.

"I've always loved carving," said Carl, "and what really helped most in convincing the elders that I was serious in learning their crafts was

170

carving a Tlingit mask which they could not distinguish from one of their own. Instead of a lot of talk and promises, it was something they could see and feel."

The Chilkat Dancers

"The dancing, though—that was the *real* breakthrough," continued Carl. "It is a perfect way for teenagers to let off steam—lively, vigorous movement with stirring chants and strong beats. They found the stories, legends, and costumes had much appeal for them, once they got interested."

They called themselves the Chilkat Dancers after the famous Chilkat Tribe, the war leaders of the Tlingit Indians. Veterans of the group will

Chilkat Dancers perform the popular "Witch Doctor's Dance" in their tribal house. They perform nightly for tourists during the summer

never forget their first Outside appearances. First they went to the Boy Scout Jamboree in 1957 at Valley Forge, Pennsylvania. Next, in 1959, they appeared at the Intertribal Indian Ceremonials, the World Series of native performers, at Gallup, New Mexico. Though beautifully costumed, the Chilkat Dancers from Port Chilkoot, Alaska nervously awaited their turn to compete. Competition was stiff; they were dancing against forty different tribes, including the Aztecs of Mexico, the Voldederos of Vera Cruz, the Apache, the Navajo, and many others. It had taken some scraping to get together enough money to make the trip, and they left Alaska with the feeling that there were some in high positions in their state who feared that the new little group might embarrass Alaska. Instead of disgrace, their fine singing and dancing won not only an ovation, but the Grand Prize!

Such honors were the encouragement they needed. The group, though with changing membership, has developed into one of Alaska's outstanding tourist attractions. A girls' auxiliary, also authentically costumed, now supplements the scout-troop dancers. Their main performing is done in their own tribal house on the parade grounds at Port Chilkoot, but they are often asked to travel to other parts of the United States as well as to foreign countries. All of the dancers are also artists and craftsmen, and they make all their own costumes.

Young Chilkat Dancers discuss their plans in Carl Heinmiller's home, remodeled from an old army building

Indian girls work on their own button blankets for Chilkat Dance. Designs are authentic

"Trying to come up with a really impressive gift for some of the cities we have visited got us started in the totem-pole carving business," Carl said. "A six-foot, authentically carved pole is quite a souvenir to leave our hosts to remember us by!"

Totem Poles Tell a Story

Again tribal leaders at nearby Klukwan were consulted, so that the finished product would be accurate, and the resulting research project proved fascinating. They learned that totems as an art form are strictly Indian on the Northwest Coast and Alaska, mainly because the Indians lived where the material needed—wood—was abundant.

They also learned why there are so few ancient totem poles standing on village sites. Though some people, exploring off the beaten track, have been lucky enough to come upon some of these monuments in various stages of decay, there are few originals left outside of museums. Wooden things do not last long exposed to the elements in this moist coastal region. The art has to be constantly practised, and most poles on

173

Alaska State Museum at Juneau probably has best Indian artifacts. Tlingit house pole (center) and shield-like objects (right) were symbols of chiefs' prestige

display have been carved by present-day Indians, or white people interested in the art. They are considered reproductions of originals. Modern carving tools and store-bought paints make the job of keeping poles in repair or replacing them much easier. However, at Klukwan, there are still about twenty houseposts at least one hundred years old, well-preserved because they have been kept inside.

Totems in the old days told a great deal to those who could read them. They have never had a religious significance, but were simply a means of reminding the viewer—with symbols and characters—of a story or happening in the past. To make sense, the story has to be already known, as well as the exclusive symbols belonging to various clans and families. With no written language and no way to record business and social

174

transactions or history, totems were a practical as well as an artistic answer.

The chief was top man on the totem pole and had an Heraldic Screen all his own, attached to the front of his main building. He might also have a name pole out front, where all could read his social standing and know his family crests. When he died, a Memorial Pole was usually erected. Chiefs also had a Ridicule or Shame Pole, to wage psychological warfare on rival chiefs or enemies. They erected it with proper descriptive carvings to depict the wrong doing of the person they wished to discredit, and it was amazing how devastating this visual—and public—chastisement could be!

The greatest rivalry developed over Potlatch Poles. They indicated the wealth of the builder, and the only limit on ingenuity and value was the amount of his possessions. To an Indian, the kind of pole erected for important festivals and rituals indicated how much that person had in his bank. Poles were also used for burial. Mortuary Poles had a hollow just large enough to receive the ashes of the deceased after cremation.

Totems were used in house construction and are still found in good shape because they were not exposed to the elements. These houseposts were often hollow shells fitted around the pillars on which the house actually rested. The decoration invariably included the owner's crests and any other items to be remembered about the family living there. If the house was rebuilt or moved, it was easy to take off the outside carving and use it on the houseposts of the new home.

"Our tribal house is patterned after what was recorded by the Museum of Natural History to be found at Klukwan and elsewhere," says Carl. "Designs are real, but the purpose in our art program is to create a piece of art, not necessarily to tell a tale as the Indians did."

Manpower Development Training Program

Though the cultural parts of the program are dearest to Carl's heart, and he is most anxious to develop the sparks of talent he finds in his young people, his work is founded on broader lines. Alaska Youth, Inc. was for many years an important and growing part of the economy of the town. There was no limitation put on membership; Carl took the youngsters as he found them. Most were wholly or part Indian, but others were from local white families with the common bond of a need to do worthwhile work and a mutual interest in Indian things.

Alaska Youth filled a real need in the community when it was started in 1957. There was work to be done, and the youngsters were available to hire out by the hour. There were cleanup jobs, construction projects, visitors to guide; the organization could usually find a boy or girl for almost any chore that came up. The more skilled craft workers were paid by the hour, a chance to earn while they learned in many cases. Alaska Youth, followed by Alaska Indian Arts, was successful because it gave a most positive type of help. The appeal to natural creative abilities developed pride in workmanship. Carl's success with helping his youngsters acquire good work habits and the tangible results, some very fine artistic products, convinced the government that a larger program should be developed at Port Chilkoot.

Thus, from Carl Heinmiller's Alaska Youth came Alaska Indian Arts, Inc., which today is the training facility for the government-sponsored Manpower Development Training program.

The Manpower Development Training program in Port Chilkoot has high goals. Objectives are to relieve unemployment in villages by developing skilled labor and to raise standards of living through arts and crafts. Dedicated leaders feel the people in these villages, caught in the transition period, have ability. The problem is to develop it and find out where they fit.

"Fishing used to be the Indians' economic mainstay around here," pointed out Carl. "They were even able to continue on, using white man's ways, till salmon became scarce and the jobs too seasonal. They need help to find other ways to make a decent living the year round."

The whole staff of the program is chosen for ability to demonstrate and teach. Besides Carl Heinmiller, director of the program, and Ted Gregg, instructor in woodwork, there are other talented staff members. Gil Smith, a famous Alaskan artist, teaches basic art and design. Ira Powell teaches silversmithing and semiprecious stone carving. Nathan Jackson and Wesley Willard, both Indian staff members, came up through the ranks of Alaska Indian Arts. After attending the American Institute of Indian Arts at Santa Fe, Nathan came back to Port Chilkoot to teach block printing.

"Nathan could be one of Alaska's best artists," Carl says. "He can do anything: carving, silver work, textiles, oils—and he is a fantastic dancer."

Bill Holm—high school art teacher, Indian dancer, and an authority on Indian art—lives in Seattle but heads for Port Chilkoot to become a guest teacher during his vacations. He also wrote the book used as a text for the Indian Arts program.

Then there is Dorothy Fossman, the wife of the Bureau of Indian Affairs teacher from Klukwan. She fills in the gaps in the native students' educational backgrounds, teaching them mathematics, English, or any other skills they lack in order to be trained at the school.

"Dorothy can get more out of these people than anyone I ever saw," marvels Carl. "If a forty-year-old student needs fifth-grade arithmetic, she can teach him!"

Ruth Hartmann, the Presbyterian preacher's wife from Haines, does the school's office work with one hand and teaches music with the other.

Part of the program is vocational rehabilitation of handicapped

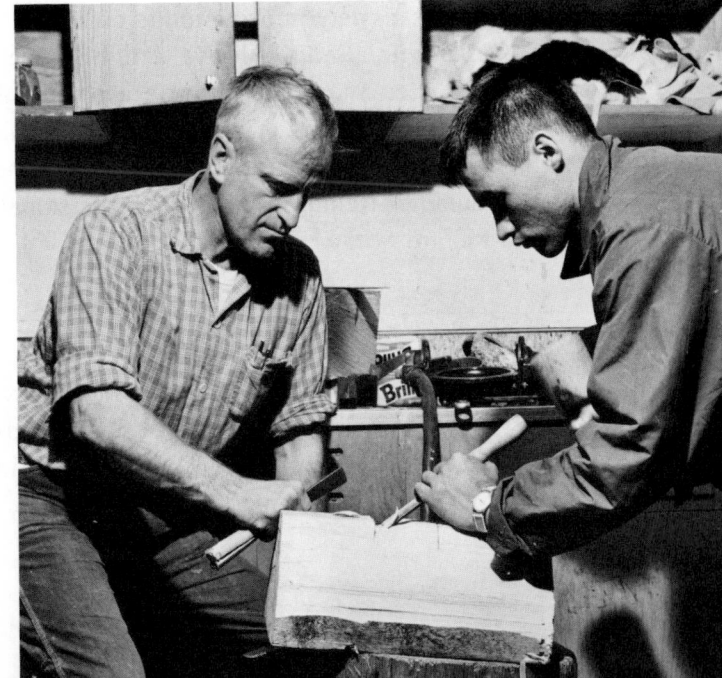

Carl Heinmiller teaches Indian student mask-carving. Yellow Alaska cedar is the preferred wood

Typical Alaska home at Skagway with three adopted Indian children. The husband is a longshoreman, city councilman, and museum director

people. Carl sets an inspirational example. In an heroic act he lost an eye and the fingers of one hand in World War II. But the handicap does not stop him from doing exquisite carving or anything else, for that matter, that he sets his determined mind to do.

Carl's wife, Betty—always active in the community—and his two children, Lee and Judy, all have a part in their father's absorbing and time-consuming work. Carl is already planning ahead to the time when there will be room for trainees from *all* Southeast Alaska villages, as well as a summer training school for professionals in teaching and in social and welfare work.

A Typically Alaskan Life

The Tresham (Ted) Gregg, Jr. family are neighbors of the Heinmillers. They also live in one of the big, square officer-quarters buildings converted to a family home. The mother, Mimi Gregg, runs a travel and craft business with a partner, Betty Moore. The father—Ted—whose specialty is woodcrafting, teaches in the new MDTA program. All four of the children have taken part in the dancing and crafts program over the years and helped their parents in the family business. The two oldest children attended colleges outside of Alaska; the two youngest attend the excellent senior and junior high schools at Haines. The whole family leads a busy, interesting, typically Alaskan life.

"I personally believe that this area is better integrated as to race than almost anywhere," said Mimi Gregg. "The races seem to get along fine. Our whole family life has been richer from rubbing shoulders with people of another culture and learning about their art."

Even guests who stay around the area for a while stand a chance of being included in a performance of the Chilkat Dancers. Carl invited all three Spring children to join the group one night. The baby bear part was open in the Bear and Raven Dance because the small child who danced the part was ill, and the smallest Spring child, Tracy, just happened to fit the genuine bearskin costume.

"She's been singing along with us every night this week; she might as well join us on stage," chuckled Carl. "That's how the youngsters used to learn the songs and dances from their elders."

Three weeks later at a camp ground near Fairbanks it was evident what the Indian baby bear had been coming down with at Port Chilkoot. Tracy broke out with a beautiful case of measles.

"The revenge was unintentional," wrote Carl. "Tell Tracy in the old days it was the other way around; the palefaces gave measles to the redskins!"

Like many other families in Haines and Port Chilkoot, both the Gregg and Heinmiller families have provided a foster home for an Indian child who had an unfortunate family background. The Indian arts program has provided a real basis for mutual understanding and working together. It has been a lifesaver and the making of some of these intelligent, talented young people. For the present, though, most of their stories are still unfinished. One tall and talented dancer, Frank Berry, is studying anthropology at the University of Alaska. Irene Sparks graduated from a teaching college Outside and has returned to teach at Bethel, Alaska. Bethel has the lowest income rate in all the United States. Irene,

Scenic Haines Highway between Port Chilkoot and Klukwan Indian Village

now married to a fellow teacher, Mike Rowan, is attempting a program similar to Port Chilkoot's Alaska Indian Arts at Bethel.

Another dancer, Charles Goodwin—talented in music—dreams of being a composer and using musical themes from his Indian heritage. Teresa Porter's blue eyes, light-brown hair, and peaches-and-cream complexion deny her half-Indian blood. Beautiful and a graceful dancer, she was a leader in her high school class. Teresa's brother, Walter is tall, dark, and well built—the picture of how an Indian brave should look. Janet Willard, niece of instructor Wesley Willard, is another charming dancer. All these young people and many more have shown much potential. What will be their destiny? And what will become of their friends, like Annette and Teddy Gregg?

180

"I can't answer for them," muses their father. "I don't know if they will come back permanently for some time, if ever. This is one of the problems of educating our children Outside. The educated youth, by and large, seems to stay out for some time."

"You have to have a dream in Alaska" reassures his daughter, Annette. "Part of growing up is thinking you want to go away and have no part of Alaska. But maturity is realizing there is no other place like it."

"I think Port Chilkoot and Haines will finally come into their own because of the location, weather and people," Mimi Gregg sums up. "This is what the traveler is looking for, what he thinks Alaska should be: high, snow-covered mountains, lush rain-forest, glaciers, and fjords. There is plenty of room to expand and almost anything can happen here—shipping, iron ore, tourists."

Iron ore is an interesting possibility. The Klukwan iron deposit appears to be a big one. Will iron mean to the Chilkats what Oklahoma oil meant to the Osage Indians?

As for tourism, the Indians are already deeply involved through song and dance, and arts and crafts. Port Chilkoot with its tribal house and its dancers and the expanding Indian Arts program is already a major Alaskan attraction. It is hoped it will be the blueprint for helping all natives become a contributing, happy, satisfied, vigorous part of the complex culture and economy of Alaska today and in the future.

The Lure of Alaska

All summer at Camp Denali, just outside the farthest boundaries of McKinley National Park, there is a constant flow of people, all responding to one of the modern-day lures of Alaska. They come from all parts of the world, arrive in every possible type of conveyance, as well as on foot; all ages, races, and nationalities come, all with a common desire: to share a true wilderness experience. The two women who own and operate the camp, Celia Hunter and Ginny Wood, and their staff are dedicated to making this possible.

Celia and Ginny are rugged individualists who love the outdoors in its primitive state and would like to keep it that way. They are happiest when involved in outdoor pursuits and sharing them with others. Over the years they have worked at a variety of interesting jobs. They were both ferry pilots in World War II, delivering everything from multi-engine transports to P-38's. After that came bush-piloting, and both have commercial air licenses.

Celia spotted Camp Denali's intriguing site while she was looking for an airstrip in the area for Wien Air Alaska. The high, remote ridge just outside the north boundary of Mount McKinley National Park overlooks a fantastic view of wilderness, wildlife, and snow-capped peaks, dominated by majestic Mount McKinley. As the two Alaskans explored the area, they asked themselves the typically Alaskan question, "How can we manage to earn a living and at the same time do work we wholeheartedly enjoy?"

"We convinced ourselves that this was just the challenge we had been looking for," said Ginny.

Guests join in songfest before dinner at Camp Denali

Starting with nothing but the magnificent setting, they would build a camp for people who would appreciate being close to nature.

"We determined to give guests a vacation in depth," said Celia, "one that they would never forget."

Camp was started in 1952, five years before the Denali Highway was engineered to McKinley Park. That meant that everything for construction or supply had to come in by plane, railroad, jeep, or backpack. It has taken years to achieve its present comfortable, but still primitive, state and a real resistance on the part of the owners to suggestions that they add certain taken-for-granted modern touches that might detract from the wilderness atmosphere they are trying to preserve.

Any improvements added over the years are carefully weighed, to be sure they will really benefit the operators and staff. Benefit, in this case, means speeding up the chores so that they have more time to play with the guests or carry on their own recreational projects. That is why water is piped into the kitchen and *Sluice-Box* cabin, where the washing and showering are done. The luxury of hot water is provided there, too, by firing up an efficient woodburning stove. However, a plastic pipe stops just short of individual cabin doors, and guests fill their own basins. Though a small generator provides ample light for kitchen, mess hall, and recreation lounge, guests carry Coleman lanterns to their cabins when they turn in for the night.

Celia and Ginny have to fight the battle of plumbing on a double front: the complaints of guests who accept the facilities but can't help

Celia Hunter (left) and Ginny Wood pioneered tourism in Alaska. They own and operate Camp Denali

Camp Denali staff doesn't get outside for haircuts. Alaskans must be self-reliant

pointing out that other means are possible, and the nature of the tundra-covered permafrost. Digging holes in permafrost is time-consuming, but not as time-consuming nor as expensive as trying to lay and keep pipes open three months in the summer. They figure some improvements at camp could only add to their troubles. Besides, helping to dig new holes as needed and construct small buildings is a fascinating experience for some city-bred guests—and the closest that many of them will ever come to real pioneering. A New York college professor and a visiting photographer built most of a modernistic outhouse, to which they pointed with pride at every opportunity until the staff threatened to name it after them.

Most of the cabins are of sturdy log-construction and they are strategically and scenically placed around the camp area. Again, the replacement of the original tent-cabins over the years was for simplifying the

185

A Disney photographer and a college student, young employees at Camp Denali, play after work

upkeep. Cabins can be shut up intact and weatherproofed against the elements at the end of the season, and the saving on canvas is considerable. Inside the cabins are wood stoves and bunk beds equipped with down sleeping bags and changeable outing flannel liners, very cozy for chilly Alaskan nights.

Besides the regular accommodations, Camp Denali has a special section called Bedrock. This was started, from the beginning of camp, out of sympathy for mountain-climbing friends on limited budgets. These hardier souls sleep in permanently pitched small tents, furnished with a cot, for little more than a song. Even Bedrock has been upgraded recently. In upper camp a log cabin replaced a large canvas tent that found its final resting place in Bedrock with a wood stove to give warmth and comfort. It has six bunks, but sleeps any number. From Bedrock has come many a staff member over the years. If you can exist there and enjoy it, you have the stuff for working on the staff.

The Staff of Camp Denali

It is no coincidence that staff members are invariably the same rugged individual type as the owners. They are recruited with care; there is always a lot to be done at camp, and teamwork is essential. Some are friends and acquaintances who started out voluntarily to help on camp projects. Others happened to be passing by from other parts of the world, liked what they saw, and stayed on.

"Some have come up through the ranks," Celia observes. "They served as guests first."

There are few places that lend themselves to research so well as Camp Denali, some staff members want to be at camp to carry on a private

Camp Denali gang and guests start a hike. Mess hall, lodge, and cabins are scattered on hillside tundra; Mount McKinley in the distance

project, often related to nature. One person may be spotting and describing nests for the Audubon Society, keeping a detailed record. Another sketches and paints every free moment. There are always a corps of photographers, amateur and often professional, snapping away; naturalists collecting and sketching specimens; and college students doing research for future use on everything from weather to animals.

The staff of eight always turns out to be an interesting group of people, whatever their purpose for being there. They are not making money, for sure; the pay is small compared to Alaskan wage-scales. But a worker there feels that dollars and cents are only a small part of the remuneration. When summer comes they feel the pull, and a nucleus from former years always manages to migrate back like the caribou, ready to face the myriad of crises that arise in wilderness living. Whenever or wherever needed they pitch in with good humor and energy. At Camp Denali it is all part of the game.

Guests at Camp Denali

Since the beginning, Camp Denali seems to attract one crisis after another. In fact, the place thrives on crises; it's part of its charm.

"Long ago, Celia and I became resigned to the fact that if something —it doesn't matter what—*can* happen at camp, or on the way in or out of camp, it *will!*" claimed Ginny.

She was thinking of road washouts, problems of supply, intricacies of keeping mechanized parts of camp running, unpredictable weather, and especially animals. Even porcupines have given them trouble; the porcupine has a special liking for the plastic, water-supply hoses and frequently shuts off the water by gnawing through the hoses. It also likes to gnaw the wooden building foundations. However, the porcupine is considered one animal that a desperate person could catch easily and survive on in the wilds, so Alaskans never destroy them.

They hesitate to shoot bears, too, though for a different reason; and this reflects the basic philosophy of camp.

"The bears were here first," they will say. "We invaded *their* territory. It's up to us to outwit, not to kill, them."

188

One-thousand-pound door at left keeps bears out of Camp Denali's storehouse

When you consider some memorable experiences with bears, you cannot help admiring the charitable attitude of the Alaskans. Most bears will avoid human beings and signs of civilization but *Ursus arctos horribilis* is not that shy. He is an educated bear, always huge, that knows his way around and where to look for the goodies near any deserted camp. His ability to ferret out food and consume it and many other supposedly non-edible items is fantastic. He is so strong that he can usually just lean on or claw through any attempts at bear-proofing.

One such bear almost put Camp Denali out of existence. One recent spring a friend, flying over the area and swooping low over the camp, noticed signs of debris and destruction and what appeared to be a whole building missing. He reported the news to Celia and Ginny. Someone landed as close as possible and then hiked in on skis for a closer look. After camp had been closed for the winter, undoubtedly a big Alaska Brownie or Toklat grizzly had paid a pre-hibernation visit to camp, and the result was a shambles. He was a big fellow that pushed a massive metal-covered door right through the jamb to get in the dining room. It looked as though he had used a combination of flour, honey, and sugar

189

for a finger-painting spree on walls and furniture. In the laundry room he merely chewed boxes of soap powder. Until his crime was reconstructed, it appeared as if he had somehow managed to consume the entire storehouse building. It was an aluminum building, with a spike-studded barricade over the bear door, locked in place by a triple cable. The bear clawed through and, while trying to consume everything within, managed to knock down and ignite a case of matches.

"Perhaps he just wanted to cook his meal," joked Celia. "Fortunately, the fire was contained in the aluminum building, which melted down, and did not spread to our nearby gas cans. Their lids were bulging, however."

In spite of this experience, the camp still holds to its one-sided, non-aggression pact with bears. However, stores are now kept in a solid log-building with a massive one thousand-pound drawbridge type of bear door, and a member of the staff always stays on long enough after camp is closed in September to bear-sit. To prevent a repetition of a disastrous per-hibernation visit, this usually means till after the snow flies, and it is necessary to ski out.

A neighboring old prospector chides Celia and Ginny about their bear trouble! He claims all he has ever had to do to protect his spread from

A yoke and huge tins are practical for carrying everything from garbage to hot water at spread-out Camp Denali

these educated bears is put a note on his door when he leaves for the winter. In it he threatens to shoot full of holes any bear that doesn't behave.

Besides the owners, it takes three men, including a mechanic, plus five women and the cook to keep camp going. Prerequisites for the cook are unusual, in that they want someone who has good organizational ability for the first qualification. They concede experience in cooking for large groups is helpful, but not essential. The cook has to be able to plan menus and be ingenious in using what's on hand. As for the rest of the staff, they have to be ready, willing, and able to cope with anything that comes up, pitching in whenever and wherever needed. These adaptive young people whip through the work with cheerful vigor, the sooner to get out on hikes and other projects.

The spirit at Camp Denali is contagious. Its informality appeals to a surprising assortment of guests, and they can join in with whatever is going on at the moment. Or if someone has a desire to do something special and he makes it known, it becomes the basis for an expedition. There are Wilderness Workshops, early morning bird-watching trips and overnight camps, photography safaris to where the big game may be observed, fishing in Moose Creek, canoeing on Wonder Lake, week long climbs to McKinley's spectacular glaciers, and even gold panning. Celia and Ginny leased the diggings of a couple of old miners at Kantishna, once a mining town of two thousand, but now a ghost. Their Friday Creek Sunday Gold Panners Association is for those who pan for fun. Invariably there is a showing of color, and that big nugget *might* show up in the next panful!

The guest book contains the names of some Rockefellers, Department of the Interior officials, United States Senators, famous mountaineers, photographers, scholars, and conservationists. One year there was a Spanish couple who flew over the Pole and then toured Alaska in a rented station wagon. That same season included some Swiss business-men, a German student on his way to spend the summer on the Juneau Ice Field, assorted Englishmen and Canadians, and a French volcanolo-gist who had been visiting the Valley of Ten Thousand Smokes. Another memorable visitor was the assistant director of the Congo National Park

System, a negro who spoke fluent French, but no English. He livened up songfests around the fireplace with his guitar-accompanied Swahili folk songs.

The Denali Highway to Mount McKinley National Park

The oldest road in Alaska is the Richardson; the longest the Alaska Highway. The Denali is the newest and can claim the title most lonesome road. It leaves the paved Richardson at the village of Paxson and winds through two hundred and fifty miles of utter wilderness. Until this barren-looking dirt road was constructed, the only other way to visit McKinley National Park was by railroad or plane.

A family that traveled this road in 1961, three years after it was opened, declared it the most deserted road they had seen in six thousand miles of travel. In the first one hundred and fifty-four miles to McKinley Park boundary they counted only seven cars. However, when they returned three weeks later, they were amazed to find this area outside the park overrun by hunters. The game warden said fourteen hundred hunters were in the vicinity, probably twenty-five hundred caribou would be taken by the first of October, when the highway would be closed by snow.

But if the Denali Highway seems short on cars and people most of the season, the wildlife is prolific. The isolated position of the road makes it ideal for animal- and bird-watching, especially after the road enters the Park, where wildlife is protected. Most of the highway is at, or above, timberline so visibility is excellent. It is easy to see a beautiful red fox as he scoots for a slight covering of scrubby brush and then quietly becomes a people-watcher for as long as they watch him. Marshy roadside lakes are a good place for moose. Black bears are likely to amble across the road in search of tasty blueberries. It takes good eyesight to spot a family of ptarmigan in somber summer dress as they scuttle ahead and then freeze to anonymity by the roadside. These birds have a perfect camouflage. Their feathers blend into varicolored summer foilage, and in winter they turn pure white to match the snowy background.

Scanning any precipitous slope is often rewarded by a view of white

Dall mountain sheep picking their way across, or instructing their young in the fine art of mountain climbing or snow sliding. One mountain pass in particular inside the Park has a sign alerting motorists to watch for the grizzly bear, the huge blonde Toklat grizzly with a humped back. Rangers tell people to stay in their cars, for often the bear may be an overly-protective mama romping with her playful cubs, just a few hundred feet off the road.

At first caribou, the most plentiful and least shy of the wild game, seem to blend in with the rolling hills of alpine tundra, but sharp eyes are soon able to separate their branched antlers from the rest of the terrain. A couple of young caribou make their headquarters just outside the new Eielson Visitors' Center; you wonder if they might be on the Park Service payroll. These wild relatives of the reindeer coyly pose for pictures, and timidly accept handouts.

The Visitors' Center, sixty-six miles beyond Park Headquarters, is the first place Mount McKinley comes into view. The weather is temperamental and some visitors have to leave without seeing the mountain at all, if it happens to be sulking in the clouds that day.

Young caribou have become somewhat tame at Eielson Visitors' Center in Mount McKinley National Park

However, inside Eielson Center are photographs, displays, and books telling about this vast National Park. Rangers visit with tourists, answer their questions, and have telescopes trained on glaciers and other interesting phenomena. There is always one prefocused on Mount McKinley should it deign to appear.

From the Center on, the highway deteriorates to a narrow, winding, and sometimes precipitous road as it heads for the far reaches of the Park boundary. It is usually passable, but with signs here and there that it might be a struggle to keep it that way. Those who keep on going to Camp Denali, just beyond the boundary, can learn all about that from owners Celia Hunter and Virginia Wood and staff. They start for camp as soon as they think they can get through; the trip always turns out to be an adventure.

"We figure reports on road conditions are rarely valid by the time we hear them, so when the time comes we just start out," explained Ginny. "We know just how those troops felt building the Alaska Highway; we can usually count on rebuilding a spot or two of the Denali before we get to camp."

When mud two feet deep stops four-wheel-drive vehicles, all hands start tossing rocks into the muck to the point where the jeep can be inched through to the other side. The other vehicles can then be winched over with the help of the jeep. However, on one famous trip, when the advance party started out with five assorted cars, trucks and jeeps, only one made it to camp in time to open up and greet guests due to arrive four days later.

Where the Denali Highway ends, Camp Denali's private road problems begin. In keeping with their idea that the wilderness setting should be marred as little as possible by signs of civilization, all cars are parked some distance away from camp. The steep road to camp itself is for utility purposes only. Even so, road and path building on permafrost is a constant chore. A typical summer's project, in addition to all the other chores and activities that go on at camp, is hauling up and spreading sixty-five truckloads of gravel around the lodge, warehouse, and dining room, and on the footpaths to cope with the mud as the frozen ground melts.

Alaska University student fills holes in Camp Denali's private road. Where else can a teen-age girl drive a bulldozer

Camp Denali represents today's most modern lure of Alaska: the appeal to the adventuresome spirit through recreation. Other lures of earlier years were just as strong, but appealed to people's other needs, desires, and emotions. Among the earlier people were found some very typical Alaskan personalities, the prototype of many Alaskans today. They just happened to live there one hundred years sooner. Some were motivated by greed, some had nobler aims. They were of many nationalities; one quality they had to have in common was stamina. A look back into Alaska's history helps one to understand better the Alaska of today.

What Lured the Russians to Alaska?

Peter the First—considered greatest of the Russian Czars—an energetic, fiery, and curious man, began to wonder about what lay to the east of Russia. Was the continent of Asia separated by sea from the continent of North America, he wondered? Were there any people living there? Since it was heretofore unexplored and therefore unknown, could it be possible this land might be of value to Russia? The only knowledge he had was from some early and rugged Siberian Cossack explorers who had brought back a few furs along with rather unfavorable tales of an icy land and a few hostile people.

A man of action, he chose someone to go exploring. Perhaps picked on would be a better way to put it; at least that seemed to be the opinion of the lucky man: Vitus Bering, a Dane and captain in the Russian navy. Peter with his drive and energy was also considered by some of his subjects a bit mad, a view no doubt shared by Bering. Even Peter's death soon afterward did not get Bering out of the assignment; Czarina Catherine was just as determined to follow through on her husband's last wishes. In 1728 the reluctant explorer took off on a two months' cruise.

"No," he stated on his return, "the two continents are not connected."

After establishing that geographical point, he probably hoped it would end the matter. But Catherine was not satisfied. There was doubt that he had actually seen the mainland of Alaska. She was not at all discouraged by his gloomy log entries describing his impressions of the land—frozen, sterile, barren wasteland.

In 1741 Bering was sent back for another, more extensive look. This time he sighted the towering Saint Elias Range of mountains on the mainland and as he turned to hurry home, a series of circumstances followed which completely altered the then-known conception of Alaska.

A violent storm shipwrecked the party, and they were forced to spend the winter on one of the islands. Bering did not survive the hardships. Many members of his crew also perished during those bitter months.

Fortunately Dr. G. W. Steller, the first mate, was a scientist whose knowledge of plants and animals and general know-how helped pull the survivors through their ordeal. In spite of Bering's earlier reports Dr. Steller had asked to go along to make a complete record of what he felt sure was a gold mine of botanical, sea, and animal specimens. Already he had proved his worth on the trip by going ashore and collecting herbs to counteract the crew's scurvy, the weakening and often fatal disease of seafaring men.

The survivors got through the winter, living on food from the sea and animals they were able to trap. With spring came new hope. The snow left and as Steller anticipated, the land became alive. He collected and catalogued his specimens while others concentrated on building a boat they hoped would take them home again.

It did, indeed, and they were greeted as if arisen from the dead, for the expedition had long been given up for lost. With them they had the botanical specimens with Dr. Steller's painstaking notes and a wealth of furs: sea otter, fur seal, and fox, which abounded on the island. To Bering must go the credit for the actual discovery of Alaska, but to Steller belongs the glory of discovery and recognition of the valuable resources there. The Steller jay, a bird common in Alaska, was named for him.

The motley crew accompanying the two must also share the blame for triggering a stampede for fur surpassed only by the stampede for gold many years later. The rush for furs marked the beginning of an era shameful in its ruthless slaughter of fur-bearing animals and unspeakably harsh exploitation of Alaska natives.

A horde of fur hunters, whose best traits may have been physical courage and energy, rushed to the Siberian coast to build boats and be first to the hunting grounds. No matter how seaworthy the boats, the foolhardy were undeterred by the prospects of shipwreck, scurvy, starvation, or death by outraged natives. For those that somehow survived the grim pitfalls the profits were great.

Even the Czarina was caught up in the excitement. What woman to this day can resist a present of a fur coat? Catherine was thrilled to receive an especially lovely fur robe made of sea otter pelts.

Realizing that something should be done about the senseless unorganized scramble, Catherine tried to reduce the chaos by encouraging Russian colonies in the new land. Homes and families, law and order, and as many civilized advantages as possible were urged for the pioneer outposts of the Russian empire.

Catherine used good judgment when she sent Alexander Baranof to straighten out affairs at one of the principal colonies. He was the right type to be a frontier leader and organizer: farsighted and energetic.

Unfortunately he was also harsh, unscrupulous, and arrogant—ruling with an iron hand and absolute power. Unpopular as he was, his rule might have been shortened by a violent end. He was fearful enough for his life that he wore a coat of mail, like a gangster's bullet-proof vest, under his clothing. He died on board ship as he was on his way back to Russia after serving twenty-five years. Rumor has it he may have been poisoned. Nevertheless, he kept things under control and built up trade. Sitka prospered as a wealthy and cultured center.

When news of a rich fur trade reached other countries, several of them tried for a toehold in Alaska. From the east came the British by way of the Mackenzie River Valley; various other nations, mainly Spanish and French, pushed from the south. But none had the success of Russia, firmly entrenched and even sending explorers down the California coast.

Russian activity in Alaska continued for almost a century and a half. Then after realizing a fortune in furs, the Russians did a rather amazing thing; they sold out to the United States. But that was another story.

The Gold Rush

Under Russian rule the wealth of Alaska in the form of blue fox, otter, and fur seal was the lure attracting traders to the newly discovered land. Several years later, after the United States bought Alaska, gold was to take over the minds and hearts of men. For one mad period in the history of Alaska at the turn of the nineteenth century, the allure of her gold—like a siren song—enticed prospectors to take their chances in the Far North.

Survival of the fittest was the law that carried some to the realization of their golden dreams; others were doomed almost from the time they made the decision to take the gamble. Of these, by far the majority, the lucky ones were those who managed to retreat—with their lives.

"You are now standing on the famous golden sands of Nome," tour guide Willy Brown announced solemnly to his group of visitors who had flown in from Anchorage that afternoon.

Everyone looked down at his feet. The sand definitely did not look golden. In fact, except for the texture, it hardly looked like the sand one

198

expects to find at the oceanside. The color was reddish-black, and any gold in it surely must have been removed in the thorough sifting of half a century ago.

"More than two million dollars' worth was taken from this sand during the gold rush," Willy continued, apparently reading his guest's thoughts. "And it's not all gone yet. Let me show you."

He produced a round pan, about a foot and a half in diameter, and using its sloping three-inch sides as a scoop, bent over and picked up a sampling of the sand at random. In his spotted hair seal jacket, mink tie, and derby hat, Willy Brown looks the part of an Alaskan "character." A long-time resident of Nome, he is well steeped in its history. His ready wit and thorough knowledge of the town enthrall his vistors on a guided tour by school bus, idled by summer, that hits most of the highlights.

Willy dipped some water from a nearby trough, squatted on his heels, and proceeded to demonstrate the art of gold panning. While he skilfully sluiced the water around in the pan, washing away dirt and sand, he carried on a running commentary on gold. Not the kind locked in solid earth ores; nor the shiny fool's gold, which isn't gold at all; but everybody's gold: shiny yellow nuggets of unbelievable size down to more common flakes of the precious metal.

"The color is beginning to show," Willy exclaimed triumphantly.

Heads bent over the gold pan, still being agitated. Sure enough, small flakes, heavier than either the sand or water were beginning to accumulate on the bottom. He continued to shake the pan and talk till, in a matter of minutes, nothing was left but the gold flakes, which he carefully guided into a small bottle.

"Hmmm, about fifty cents worth," he estimated, examining the vial with a practiced eye. "Almost make wages today."

Nome was the setting of the novel *The Spoilers* by Rex Beach, who witnessed the gold scramble, and then made *his* fortune writing about it. Willy's comment on the book was to the point, as usual.

"Anyone who really wants to know what went on in Nome in those days should read *The Spoilers*. The only fiction about it was the names used. Even so, the events and descriptions were so true to life that everyone knew who the author had in mind."

Though there had been glimmers of gold in the Nome area as long ago

Main street of Nome. By 1899 it was a tent town of twenty to thirty thousand gold seekers

as the 1860's, the height of the influx of gold seekers came in 1899. This was two or three years after three lone prospectors discovered gold along Anvil Creek and spent one cold, delirious night panning eighteen hundred dollars' worth with water kept in running form by heating it over their campfire. Such news could not be kept secret and the leak spread down to Seattle via a newspaper headline advertising "A ton of gold!"

Boats of all descriptions headed for Nome in the summer, the only time the sea would be free of ice. Even so, landing was a problem with no docks, and boats had to anchor far out in the bay. Supplies had to be ferried in to be dumped on the beach. Sometimes there were as many as seventy boats anchored out at a time, waiting to unload their cargo.

The town of Nome grew lengthwise along the beach, as that was where the gold was most available. By 1899 it was a tent town of twenty or thirty thousand people, with elbow-to-elbow claims stretching for thirty-five miles along the shores of the Bering Sea. Letters to a friend at the far end of town were mailed by passing them from hand to hand till they reached the right person. An answer could be expected in three days.

200

"That gold fever was contagious," Willy Brown concluded. "It still is. Everyone who comes to Alaska finds he has a touch of the prospector in him, sooner or later." It is a weekend, pay-as-you-play hobby for many.

Early Schools Under the American Flag

Where gold and other riches may have brought out the worst in people, education brought out the best. The field of education provided a philanthropic challenge for various religious groups as well as individuals who went to Alaska. Those interested in furthering education were a determined, stubborn, intelligent part of the population. They had to be in those days to make progress under difficult circumstances.

Fortunately those interested in educating Alaskans after the purchase did not sit around waiting for that first territorial legislature to convene. That would have meant almost a fifty-year wait. People determined to be permanent residents of Alaska realized the importance of schooling for their children and were willing to assume the responsibility.

Education, however, suffered from the same growing pains as many other civic developments in Alaska. Financing was always a problem. School officials had as much trouble as politicians trying to communicate with Congress, especially when the subject was money. Educators tried to spell out the basic and growing needs in the territory, but those who handled the purse strings failed to read them. Appropriations, if any, were never adequate. Another continuing obstacle was the great distance that had to be traveled to supervise existing, but far-flung, schools. The only means of transportation, and therefore communication, were slow and inadequate.

Much credit for making up the financial deficit and for pitching in and establishing schools must go to various religious denominations. They took over where Congress left off and bridged the gap till the territory achieved enough self-government to allow for financing of civic needs. Russian mission schools continued to operate. Moravian and Swedish schools were granted permission to establish in outlying communities. Presbyterian, Episcopal, Catholic, Methodist, Baptist, Congregational, and Friends church groups all set up schools, going to Alaska in approximately that order.

One school deserves special mention, partly because of the individual for whom it was named—Sheldon Jackson. His efforts on behalf of education before the turn of the century were far-reaching, long-lasting, and almost superhuman. Though he was born a hundred years too soon to be able to take part in today's jet-age frontier, chances are he would have been right at home. His drive, personality, energy, and individualism put him in the ranks of all true Alaskans.

Sheldon Jackson school was first established as a Presbyterian Mission School in 1878. It is still going strong in Sitka today, though over the years its function has changed with the times. The interesting facts are that this school has spanned all the educational efforts under the United States flag. First started as a boys' school, it was later coeducational, became a high school in 1917, then a junior college in 1944. At present it is both a terminal school for Alaskan educational requirements and a college preparatory school. Its museum houses a fine collection of Russian relics and native arts and crafts items; its library is noted for rare books on early Pacific Northwest explorations.

Sheldon Jackson, who had already established Presbyterian mission schools in Alaska, was appointed to administer and coordinate the educational efforts in Alaska after the Congressional Act of 1884. He was also the unanimous choice of all organizations in Alaska interested in furthering education.

Jackson was given a chance to prove his merit immediately. Congress, with typical disregard for timing, appropriated too little money too late. The appropriation was not available till after the last vessels of summer had sailed for western Alaska. And so Jackson chartered his own ship to get his teachers and supplies to their schools. This exciting trip in uncharted waters and, by then, uncertain weather took one hundred and four days! But the 1886-87 school year got underway, though somewhat delayed.

Educatonal leaders of the calibre of Sheldon Jackson helped pave the way for the fine modern schools in Alaska today. Figures show that youngsters have the opportunity to stay in school longer than in many

Library of modern Glacier Valley School near Juneau

other parts of the United States. The average number of years spent in school is over twelve.

The same lures: adventure, wealth, wide open-spaces and opportunities for service that existed one hundred years ago still exist today. What is happening to them in the changing picture of Alaska?

The Changing Picture in Alaska

The increasing number of people drawn to Alaska indicates that the appeal is as strong as ever. However, attitudes are changing. Alaskans realize it is time to guard and use wisely *all* the resources of Alaska, from people to polar bears. These resources include the tangible, income-giving ones: fish, fur, gold, copper, timber, oil, and gas, as well as the intangibles: beauty to appreciate and an opportunity for soul-satisfying recreational pursuits.

"There is hope for the world's future if nations are willing to meet and discuss the future of an animal," remarked Alaska Senator E. L. (Bob) Bartlett.

Representatives of five nations had just concluded a meeting on the University of Alaska campus at Fairbanks to exchange information and consider ways of conserving polar bears. The United States, Canada, Denmark (Greenland), Norway, and the Soviet Union all own some polar-bear country and fear that modern hunting methods may be destroying nature's balance to the point where this arctic resource could become extinct.

If nations can get together to discuss and agree on polar-bear policy, perhaps the effort will carry over and apply to other areas of international relations. Alaska is becoming more involved with other nations through trade and transportation. Polar routes already have shortened distances from this country to Europe. In the future, the speed of Supersonic jets promises to whittle down the size of the world even more.

This dock at Valdez was destroyed by the Good Friday earthquake and tidal wave in 1964

Alaska's position on the map, once thought to be isolated, now appears to be in the center of transportation activity. Her military importance, both for defense and offense, continues.

What Happened to the Gold Fever?

Gold mining continued to flourish during the early 1900's. Small prospecting outfits were continually looking for a bonanza, a sudden discovery of a rich claim. Large companies invested capital for discovering where the gold-bearing ore lay, and for developing more efficient ways of mining it. Gold dredges became a symbol of Alaska along with the prospector and his pick and shovel.

Until recently, one could still drive to an area where a huge dredge might be working in the vicinity of Nome or Fairbanks. Now, however, most of these monster machines sit idle in their artificial lake, the mountains of rock-tailings scarring the countryside behind them.

The main reason for the decline of gold mining is the cost of production. Though the price of gold has not changed since 1933, the costs of mining and smelting it have trebled and quadrupled. It just doesn't pay to mine gold in Alaska at the present time.

"If you ask me, I think it's a lot of work for nothing," drawled a guide showing a group of visitors the largest gold dredge still operating at Cripple Creek a few years ago. "I'll tell you why."

This he proceeded to do—in detail. The fellow, a long-time miner, had worked in almost every phase of the operation. He told how powerful hoses were needed for hydraulic mining to wash the pay dirt down. He explained how the dredge floated slowly forward on its lake, the endless chain of buckets scooping up mouthfuls of dripping, gold-containing, coarse gravel. From the vantage point high above the dredge he took them through the process step by step: the washing, the settling of the gold in the riffles, and the periodic removal of the raw gold to the smelter under armed guard. The listeners sweated through the whole complicated, fiery smelting process to the point where, at last, the gold had been refined and cast into bricks, deceptively heavy for their size.

"And *then* what happens to it?" He paused dramatically. "Back into the ground at Fort Knox!"

Big gold dredge at Cripple Creek leaves strings of tailings. This dredge recently stopped working

Even though gold mining at present is in a dormant stage, it still has a romantic appeal to Alaskans and visitors to the state. Since 1935, there has been a course in prospecting offered by the University of Alaska. There is good reason to encourage prospecting—not only for gold but for other important minerals. It is believed that hidden somewhere in the big state are most of the strategic metals the United States needs. Important minerals like copper, tin, lead, iron, mercury, beryllium, and zinc as well as semi-precious stones are high on the list.

Though most students admit that their hearts beat a little quicker at the prospect of discovering a rich gold claim, by the time they complete the course they are also alerted to the high values of less-romantic, other finds. Methods taught still include some of those used by early gold prospectors: lots of hiking, digging, high hope and patience, along with the use of modern technical apparatus.

Tourists, a New Kind of Gold Mine

Alaskans involved in various phases of the new and fast-growing tourist industry feel that the loss of income from mined gold is being offset by tourist dollars.

207

"Fantastic to think that Alaska might some day be the crossroads of the world?" queries Mike Miller of the Travel Division of the state's Department of Economic Development and Planning. "How about a round-the-world road by way of Alaska with a tunnel across the Bering Strait? After all, there were some who thought the Alaska Highway couldn't possibly be built and maintained!"

Roads, including the unusual Marine Highway, in very recent years have played a large part in making Alaska more available to the car traveler. It is conceivable that some day car-campers will be standing in line to pay toll across the Strait, in order to travel through Asia and Europe, a reversal of the traffic pattern of thirty-five thousand years ago.

"Heaven forbid!" say some Alaskans, horrorstruck at the picture of their wilderness state being invaded by hordes of people. But the start has been made. It may be less time than they think before such a picture becomes a reality.

The Role of Education

"The changing educational picture is not filled with basically new ideas," pointed out Earle E. Costello, project director of the new William E. Beltz Vocational School in Nome. "Even the Russians felt that natives were needed to do the jobs that were to be done in the colonies in Alaska. They worked at educating them to become an important part of the economy and labor force."

Today it is even more important for all natives—Eskimos, Indians and Aleuts—to be absorbed fully into Alaska's mainstream. Partly for the sake of a healthy economy, *all* citizens need to work toward being assets instead of welfare liabilities. Mainly, however, natives are needed right in their own villages to perform the new jobs and earn the money to enable them to maintain a good standard of living in a changing culture. The role of education is to help them to help themselves.

"The modern Beltz school is attended only by natives, and some white residents resent this discrimination," continued Mr. Costello. "Actually, the school is open to all without regard to race, creed, color, or national origin."

He then explained that the school draws from all the villages of northern and southwestern Alaska. The recruiting is done in predominantly Eskimo villages; therefore the quota is likely to be filled by Eskimos.

"The MDTA school at Port Chilkoot under Carl Heinmiller serves the Southeast, so their students are mostly Indian," Mr. Costello continued. "There are examples of this segregation in many large cities in the United States. Distribution of the racial population determines the racial makeup of a school."

The government, concerned about the plight of all natives caught between two cultures authorized the Demonstration Manpower Project. The idea is not to relocate natives, but train them in lines of work which are necessary to improve the standards of living in their own villages. For example, the native people have shown they are interested in getting modern conveniences like washing machines, radios, and even television.

Past and future are represented in housing in Fairbanks. Historic log cabins are scattered through the town

"Discovery," a small replica of a Yukon River steamer, gives tourists a delightful trip on the Chena and Tanana Rivers

But it takes money to buy these things—money that is not available on their hunting-fishing subsistence economy. Even if they managed to purchase one of these coveted items, what if it breaks down? It is costly to send it Outside for repair; it might as well rust on the beach. There are, however, examples of efficient adaptation to modern machines—from complete native maintenance of airplanes landing freight and people in the villages to assembling and repairing all sorts of motorized conveniences.

The vocational training school has to be a grass-roots program. Starting at this particular time as native Alaskans are shifting gears, it has to be for trainees of all ages, even overcoming the language barrier when necessary. Trainees will have to know English well enough to be able to read and follow directions in their chosen fields. At the present time, notices of the training program are given in both the native language and English.

Much effort has gone into selecting trainees. There have been many consultations with teachers, priests, and elders of the village. The students selected come to Nome and live at the school while being trained, and then return to their native villages to make use of their training.

The Demonstration Manpower Project is an idealistic program which is in the experimental stage. It is a sincere effort to help natives adjust to a dollar economy, without changing their basic values. Changes are inevitable and must seem shattering to people used to a primitive pace of life. It would be a real tragedy to stand by and watch the disintegration of the closely knit and affectionate family units of the native Alaskans. In fact, the whole native community is a closely welded group of people dependent on one another. How else could they survive in their harsh habitat?

"We have high hopes that the school will be a real breakthrough in helping Eskimos, Aleuts, and Indians help themselves," commented Mr. Costello. "Only time will tell whether we are setting the pattern for future schools of this nature in other parts of Alaska."

The Changing Picture in the Use of Land

"The time has come when people have to live *with,* not *off* the land," is the conclusion of Justice William O. Douglas of the United States Supreme Court.

Preserving wilderness areas for future generations to enjoy has been a life-long concern of Justice Douglas. From his own personal observation he knows that, even when a relatively small number of people go into the wilderness, it becomes that much less of a wilderness. From his law practice he sees the wisdom of protecting the rights of both majority and minority groups. His Wilderness Bill of Rights expresses the need to allow for a wilderness experience for the vast majority of car-travelers as well as that small, more rugged minority who prefer to walk. The latter fear that the time is fast approaching when there will be no more true wilderness left for those willing and able to hike into it.

Justice Douglas's ideas apply more urgently to other parts of the United States at the present time, but Alaska is listening. With vast wilderness areas still intact, it is not too soon to start thinking of the future of Alaska.

There are scientific reasons for being concerned about the future of the Alaskan wilderness. Ecologists, scientists who study what happens to plants and animals in a changing environment, look at Alaska and see Scotland or Scandinavian countries as they were eight hundred or one thousand years ago. The land in these countries was still untouched then, and the human population was small. Ecologists predict that the influx of people occurring in Alaska today will scar the land even sooner. They feel that unless great conservation effort is made, animals and vegetation will become extinct, and the last remaining wilderness lost.

Those who settled in Alaska in the first place because of its most noted commodity—wide open spaces—do not want this to happen. There is still plenty of elbow room—so far. Many of these people believe that Alaska's greatest future value will be as a state of recreation. It could be one of the few places left where people can go to enjoy a genuine wilderness, provided it is carefully preserved with that in mind.

The question of building the Rampart Dam across the Yukon River caused a furious debate. It would create an artificial lake the size of Lake Erie; in about fifty years it would be ready to dispense a great deal of

Permafrost must be thawed with steam to give Nome its first water and sewer system

electric power. In the long run, would this mighty project be the making of Alaska, or the destruction of its best assets?

"There are other dam sites where less damage would be done," stated a member of the Alaska Conservation Society. "Calling the Yukon Flats a worthless swamp whose best purpose could be served by burying it under hundreds of feet of water must have been said with no appreciation of either ecology or nature."

"Recent research shows that nuclear power will be available. The Rampart Dam will be obsolete almost before they start to build it!" added an editor and outdoor enthusiast.

"Nowhere in the history of water development in North America have the fish and wildlife losses anticipated from a single project been so overwhelming," remarked a Congressman.

"A fifty-year project like the Rampart Dam will bring much-needed dollars into Alaska," argued another statesman. "People are more important than pinfeathers."

"There is no way to use up wilderness—destroying bird and animal life—and still have it for future generations," answered a Senator.

And so the people of Alaska, who are her greatest resource in this rapidly changing jet-age frontier, will have to weigh all decisions and then try to pick the wisest course. They are aware that Alaska's economy needs to be built on a sound foundation. The bonanza dreams of past eras have to be replaced by long-range goals for the overall good of the state.

It may be some time yet before all of Alaska's resources are even discovered, to say nothing of being used up. Today's philosophy warns, "Conserve, instead of always taking out of the land."

Moreover, Alaskans are in no hurry to change the many things they like about their state. As they say at Camp Denali, "This is what we like about Alaska: the land, the climate, the elements are neither for nor against you. They are just there, for a person to cope with and measure up to, if he can."

Highlights in Alaskan History

About 25,000 to 35,000 years ago, at the end of the glacier period, man migrated to the North American continent by way of the Bering Sea, scientists say.

1578	A Cossack chieftan heard of rich furs to the east and made the first excursions across the steppes, starting Russian conquest in the direction of Alaska.
1728	Vitus Bering sailed through Bering Strait for Czar Peter the Great and proved Asia and America were not joined.
1741	Bering was sent to continue explorations and officially discovered the Alaska mainland.
1784	First permanent Russian settlement in America established near Kodiak.
1808	By this date, Russian capital was established at Sitka.
1832	First discovery of gold in Alaska in vicinity of Kuskokwim River.
1848	American whalers invade the Arctic.
1867	Russia sold Alaska to the United States.
1871	Prospectors outfitted at Wrangell and sought gold up the Stikine River.
1880	Gold discovered at Silver Bow Basin by Joe Juneau and Dick Harris. Town of Juneau grew at the site.
1884	The "District of Alaska" was created by Congress.
1896	Gold discovered on the Klondike, in Canada's Yukon Territory, starting Alaska gold rushes and booming access points like Skagway and Yukon River towns.
1899	Gold discovered at Nome.

1900	Railway completed from Skagway to headwaters of Yukon River over White Pass.
1902	Gold discovered near Fairbanks, booming the access town of Valdez. The Valdez Trail to Fairbanks was forerunner of Richardson Highway.
1909	Alaska-Yukon-Pacific Exposition at Seattle.
1912	Alaska graduated from "district" to "territory" and Mt. Katmai on the Alaska Peninsula blew its top.
1913	The Territorial Legislature held its first meeting.
1914	Congress voted to construct a railroad from Seward to Fairbanks. Completed in 1923.
1916	First Alaska Statehood Bill presented to Congress by Alaskan Delegate James Wickersham.
1942	Alaska invaded by the Japanese; Alaska Highway rushed through as a defense measure.
1956	Alaska State Constitution adopted in anticipation of statehood.
1958	Congress passed Statehood Act, which was then ratified by Alaska voters.
1959	Alaska officially became the 49th state, on January 3.
1964	Good Friday earthquake, particularly destructive in the Anchorage area.
1967	Centennial of the Purchase of Alaska.

A Reading List

NON-FICTION

Alaska by Byron Fish and Bob & Ira Spring. Seattle: Superior Publishing Co., 1965. An up-to-date picture book of Alaska as it is today.

Alaska: The Big Land by Ben Adams. New York: Hill & Wang, 1959. Written by a newspaperman, one of the first to sum up the state after achieving statehood.

The Alaska Book. Chicago: J. G. Ferguson, 1960. Articles compiled from *The Alaska Sportsman Magazine.*

Alaska, An Empire in the Making by John J. Underwood. New York: Dodd, Mead & Co., 1913. This may be hard to find, except in an old book'store, but worth reading for the picture it gives of early-in-the-century Alaska.

Alaska Cookbook by Bess Cleveland. Berkeley, Cal.: Howell-North, 1960. The ingredients for some dishes may be hard to find unless you live in Alaska, but the directions are good—for many would-be cooks, young or old

Alaska: The Land and the People by Evelyn Butler and George Dale. New York: Viking, 1957. Interesting and informational by man and wife who lived and worked in Alaska.

Alaska Past and Present by Clarence Hulley. Portland, Ore.: Binsford & Mort, 1953, rev. 1958. Complete, interesting and authentic history up to statehood.

Alaska in Transition by George W. Rogers. Baltimore: Johns Hopkins Press, 1960. A study by a real authority on what's happening in Southeast Alaska during this time of basic change.

Eskimo Adventure by Edward L. Keithahn. Seattle: Superior Publishing Co., 1963. Fascinating, often amusing account of a school-teaching couple's experiences in the mid-twenties at Shishmaref, Eskimo village far to the north along the Arctic Coast.

Eskimo Cook Book. Anchorage: Alaska Crippled Children's Assn., 225 E St. Price 60c. Prepared in 1952 by Shishmaref Day School pupils. You won't find *these* ingredients at the corner store, but it is a charming little paperback book and interesting reading. Recipes were gleaned from their elders who remember the old days, and told in children's own style.

The Future of Alaska by George W. Rogers. Baltimore: Johns Hopkins Press, 1962. Mr. Rogers' second volume on the changing status of Alaska goes through statehood and discusses what happens to both people and resources.

I Am Eskimo Aknik My Name by Paul Green and illustrated by George Ahgupuk. 1959. Customs and life in the Arctic told in Eskimo style.

Monuments in Cedar by Edward L. Keithahn. Seattle: Superior Publishing Co., 1963. Mr. Keithahn was for many years the able curator of the Territorial

216

and then State Museum at Juneau. Authentic stories of totem poles, where found, and their meanings.

Northwest Coast Indian Art by Bill Holm. Seattle: Univ. of Washington Press, 1966. Excellent text for art students interested in Indian designs. This is the one being used for reference at the school Alaska Indian Arts program at Port Chilkoot.

Quoth the Raven by O. M. Salisbury. Seattle: Superior Publishing Co., 1962. First-hand account of school teaching couples' life in Indian village at Klawock during the 1920's. Much human interest, as teachers become involved with all community life, not just teaching the three R's.

The Race to Nome by Kenneth A. Ungermann. New York: Harper, 1963. Dramatically and accurately tells the whole story of the famous dogsled run to take serum to isolated and diphtheria-stricken Nome.

Russian America by Hector Chevigny. New York: Viking, 1965. Carefully researched history telling what Alaska was like under the Russians.

The State of Alaska by Ernest Gruening. New York: Random, 1954. Written by a former governor and now Alaska State Senator, this is an important book for understanding the events and procedures leading up to the Statehood goal.

The Story of Alaska by C. L. Andrews. Caldwell, Ida.: The Caxton Printers, Ltd., 1944. This book may be hard to find but contains authentic history.

Wilderness Bill of Rights by Justice William O. Douglas. Boston: Little, Brown, 1965. This first came out in the Britannica "Book of the Year" 1965.

FICTION

Call of the Wild by Jack London. Story of Buck, gold-rush dog.

The Iron Trail by Rex Beach. Based on attempts to build the railroad in Valdez-Richardson Highway area.

Poems by Robert W. Service. Most famous are "Spell of the Yukon" and "Shooting of Dan McGrew" but many others tell about the gold-rush period and the people who "moiled for gold."

Alaska Challenge by Tom E. Clarke. New York: Lothrop, 1959.

Puddle Jumper by Tom E. Clarke. New York: Lothrop, 1960.

Two modern tales of teen-agers in Alaska.

MAGAZINES

The Alaska Sportsman Magazine, Box 1271, Juneau, Alaska 99801. 50c a copy or $5.00 a year. This monthly really tells all that's going on from "Ketchikan to Barrow" as one of their departments is called. Unsophisticated and utterly fascinating.

The Milepost, Box 1271, Juneau, Alaska 99801. Price $1.95. This is brought up to date yearly and is a "must" for anyone planning a car tour to Alaska. All the information you need to know and what you'll find mile by mile on the highways. Very useful.

Index

About the Author

NORMA SPRING, her photographer husband Bob, and their three children agree that Alaska is their favorite travel area outside their home state of Washington. They have been going there ever since 1952. Bob Spring, the author's husband, has photographed almost every part of the state on an assignment or free-lance basis. As chief caption-writer and mother of three children busy asking questions, it was inevitable that Norma would write this book.

The Springs have one native-born Alaskan in their family, a husky dog adopted at the age of two months from her home in the shadow of Mt. McKinley, a favorite camping spot for the Spring family.

BOB and IRA SPRING are twin brothers who began their career as photographers at the age of twelve when they received a camera during Kodak's fiftieth anniversary celebration. They specialize in pictures of mountains, so Alaska with its snow capped peaks was a welcome assignment. Most of the pictures for this book were taken by Bob Spring. However, the twins always receive joint credit to avoid confusion.

World Neighbors

Written to introduce the reader to his contemporaries in other lands and to sketch the background needed for an understanding of the world today, these books are well-documented, revealing presentations. Based on first-hand knowledge of the country and illustrated with unusual photographs, the text is informal and inviting. Geographical, historical, and cultural data are woven unobtrusively into accounts of daily life. Maps, working index, chronology, and bibliography are useful additions.

ALASKA Pioneer State, By Norma Spring

AUSTRIA AND SWITZERLAND Alpine Countries, by Bernadine Bailey

BRAZIL Awakening Giant, by Kathleen Seegers

CANADA Young Giant of the North, by Adelaide Leitch

CENTRAL AMERICA Lands Seeking Unity, by Charles Paul May

CHILE Progress on Trial, by Charles Paul May

CHINA AND THE CHINESE, by Lyn Harrington

EQUATORIAL AFRICA New World of Tomorrow, by Glenn Kittler

GREECE & THE GREEKS, by Lyn Harrington

INDIA Land of Rivers, by L. Winifred Bryce

ISRAEL New People in an Old Land, by Lily Edelman

ITALY Modern Renaissance, by Arnold Dobrin

JAPAN Crossroads of East and West, by Ruth Kirk

MEXICO Land of Hidden Treasure, by Ellis Credle

THE SOVIET UNION A View from Within, by Franklin Folsom

THE UNITED KINGDOM A New Britain, by Marian Moore

VIETNAM and Countries of the Mekong, by Larry Henderson

SCANDINAVIA A Way of Life, by Harvey Edwards

THE WEST INDIES Islands in the Sun, by Wilfred Cartey